SWEDISH INNOVATIONS

NECESSITY is the mother of invention, according to the old saying. However, it takes more than that for an invention to achieve commercial success as an innovation. Knowledge and technical competence are also necessary partners in this process. In addition, of course, there must be an openness to the possibilities of business.

Sweden's natural environment, harsh and yet rich in natural resources, as well as the country's constantly increasing need for energy, communication, tools and machines, have been strong driving forces behind innovative work in all of these areas. Compared to many other countries, Sweden's system of compulsory elementary education was established relatively early. Beginning in the 1800s, elementary schools played an important role in providing people from all social backgrounds with an opportunity to devote themselves to the pursuit of knowledge and inventive action. Education gave self-confidence and courage, and developed people's capacity to describe new technical ideas or concepts.

The technical competence of Sweden's researchers and inventors, and their interest in technology has been of great importance for the development of Swedish society. Many of Sweden's early inventors were also discoverers; curiosity and practicality were thus combined.

This interest in technology and inventing, which in Sweden led to a culture of engineering, has been especially lively. At international level, Sweden is considered to be a true nation of engineers. Swedish technology is continually being extended into new areas of creativity and service to humanity. The comprehensive nature of Swedish inventorship is also reflected in statistics, which show that in relation to population size Sweden has one of the highest number of patents and patent applications registered in the world.

The successful realization of an innovation requires the capacity to understand and satisfy the needs of the users, as well as the technical talent for inventing. In Sweden, persistent innovative work resulted not only in interesting products, but also in business ventures which in some cases came to dominate the world market.

This book examines the variety and strength of areas in which innovations and innovators from Sweden continue to be of importance. More than just a list of interesting people and historical examples from creative milieus, this book should also serve as a source of inspiration to inventors, innovators and technologically interested people around the world. It offers a perspective on the work of Swedish inventors and innovators stretching from the beginnings of the modern era into this new millennium.

LENA TORELL

PROFESSOR, PRESIDENT OF THE ROYAL SWEDISH ACADEMY OF
ENGINEERING SCIENCES (IVA)

CONTENTS

PATENTS

A patent is a legally protected sole right granted for a certain period of time that allows the holder to exploit an invention. Patents protect technological solutions (products), methods and uses. To prevent corporations from holding patents that they do not use, Sweden limits patents to a period of 20 years (25 years for pharmaceutical products). To keep patents active, the Swedish authorities charge patent holders an annual fee determined on a progressive scale.

In Sweden, patent seekers apply to the Patent and Registration Office (PRV, Patent-och registreringsverket) which determines whether the application fulfills the necessary conditions. PRV receives about 5,000 patent applications per year, a considerable number in relation to the size of Sweden's population. Most of these are submitted by a small number of major corporations, and the remainder come from smaller companies and individuals. At international level, Sweden is a member of the Patent Cooperation Treaty (PCT) which covers 115 nations, and the European Patent Convention (EPC), which facilitates the patent application process in other countries.

Ranking of Swedish companies with the most patents applied for in 2001:
1: LM Ericsson
2: AstraZeneca
3: ABB
4: SAAB
5: SCA
6: Sandvik
7: Scania
8: Pharmacia
9: Allgon
10: SKF
11: Telia
12: Bio Vitrum

Swedish Patents	1994	1995	1996	1997	1998	1999	2000
Applications submitted	4,588	4,313	4,855	4,938	4,625	4,870	4,936
Patents granted	2,082	1,541	1,581	2,249	2,769	2,714	2,126
Patents pending at year-end	23,240	21,023	19,491	18,916	18,947	19,255	19,103

SOURCES: SWEDISH STATISTICAL YEARBOOK AND EUROPEAN PATENT OFFICE (EPO).

SOME TERMS

Several of the Swedish people mentioned in this book represent one or more of the categories explained below

Discoverers—find useful principles (theories and observations) in nature, e.g. Carl Wilhelm Scheele, who discovered oxygen, chlorine, molybdenum and other elements.

Inventors—create patentable technological principles or ideas, e.g. Sigvard Johansson, inventor of the Haldex All-Wheel Drive coupling.

Innovators—create technology or devices accepted by users or customers, e.g. Jonas Wenström, an innovator in the field of electricity, who invented the three-phase electrical system.

Entrepreneurs—design products, artifacts and/or services and introduce them onto the market, e.g. Ruben Rausing, who developed and marketed plastic-coated cartons for liquid products.

Developers—adapt new technical ideas and principles to the needs of users, customers and the market, e.g. Jöns Jacob Berzelius, who developed the first table of atomic weights.

Industrialists—establish the manufacture and distribution of new products on an industrial scale, e.g. Lars Magnus Ericsson, who established large-scale production of telephones and other equipment.

M A N Y well-known innovations and discoveries, both modern and historical, have Swedish origins. The ideas of Sweden's inventors, researchers and innovators have laid the foundations for industries and corporations, which have in turn played an important role in Sweden's industrialization and development into a modern welfare state.

Innovations come in many forms. This book presents technical products and methods which have achieved great commercial success and which, in the eyes of the law, represented a sufficiently high degree of innovation to be granted patents. We see many of these on a daily basis as consumer products, but the following account will also mention innovations that have become very important to the business sector as producer products. Swedish marketing innovations such as IKEA or the Hennes & Mauritz clothing stores do not fall within the scope of this study, nor do innovations such as the latest models offered by Volvo or Saab, or the Öresund bridge between Sweden and Denmark.

Many of Sweden's leading corporations, such as ASEA (today ABB), Ericsson, SKF, Sandvik and Alfa Laval, were built upon ideas from the late 1800s and early 1900s. Examples of well-known Swedish products from this era include the adjustable wrench, the Primus stove, AGA lighthouses and cream separators, to name but a few.

In the 20th century Swedish innovations and developments in the engineering industry remain important but in the second half of the 1900s they have experienced keen competition from the medical and pharmaceutical industries, electronics and other high-technology fields.

This book gives an insight into some of the more recent Swedish innovations that have taken on great significance and reached the international market. It will also look back in history to the days of Sweden's "Universal Geniuses" and their discoveries and inventions.

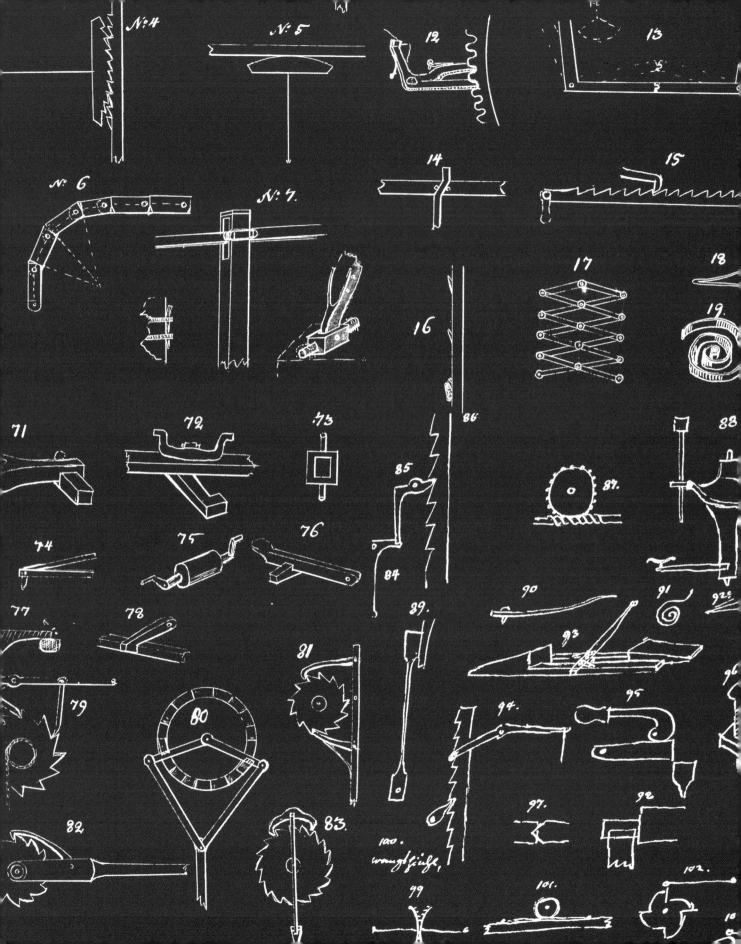

THE SWEDISH SCIENTIFIC REVOLUTION

In Sweden the scientific "revolution" occurred during the 1700s, a period when the nation was almost exclusively agricultural. The technological progress made during the 1500s and 1600s was mainly the result of the immigration of skilled handcrafters, merchants and other tradespeople, chiefly from Germany, Scotland, the Netherlands, France and the Walloon region of southern Belgium. Rich natural resources such as iron, timber and water power also contributed to these developments.

1739, the year when the Royal Swedish Academy of Sciences (Kungliga Vetenskaps-akademien, KVA) was founded, is usually regarded as the birth date for natural sciences in Sweden. Of course, study of the natural world had been pursued previously in Sweden but it was not until the 1700s that this research became systematically organized. Initially, the Royal Swedish Academy of Sciences had economic difficulties, but in October 1747 the organization was granted the privilege of publishing almanacs, which provided it with a stable economic base. This monopoly on almanacs lasted until 1972.

The scientists who were active during the 1600s and 1700s are often regarded as "universal geniuses," and they were of great importance for scientific and technological developments in Sweden. The following names are well worth noting.

LEFT: POLHEM'S "TECHNICAL ALPHABET." SKETCHES FROM THE NOTEBOOK OF HIS PUPIL CARL JOHAN CRONSTEDT IN 1729.

OLOF RUDBECK THE ELDER

Olof Rudbeck the Elder (1630–1702), a medical doctor, naturalist and archaeologist, began as a student at Uppsala University in 1648 and devoted himself to medical studies with such success that as a 22 year-old in 1652, he publicized his epoch-making discovery of the human lymphatic system. Already at this young age his reputation was so great that he was offered positions outside Sweden. However, throughout his life he remained faithful to Uppsala, where he worked tirelessly for the renewal of the university and made his mark on the academic world of his time.

He founded Sweden's first botanical garden, which he filled with plants mostly from the Netherlands at his own expense. After only a few years, the garden was home to over one thousand plants.

Rudbeck was one of Sweden's most versatile pioneers. He championed the establishment of technical schools, built bridges, constructed water systems, and taught in subjects such as mathematics, astronomy, mechanics, anatomy, architecture and structural engineering. Within each of these areas he made important contributions, some of which were pioneering.

One of his students was Christopher Polhem, whom he later collaborated with and had great influence upon.

CHRISTOPHER POLHEM

Christopher Polhem (1661–1751) lived in a time when it was still possible for an individual to master a large portion of human knowledge. His ideas had a considerable impact upon the technological developments of his day. Over the course of his 90-year life Polhem produced a huge number of inventions and ingenious designs. He built his machines himself and carried out many of his projects on his own.

In 1697 the Swedish Mining Collegium granted funds for Sweden's first Laboratorium Mechanicum. The technical drawings, models and experimental equipment which it would contain were to be used as instructional materials for technical education. Some of these models, as well as Polhem's "technical alphabet," are preserved in the Museum of Science and Technology in Stockholm.

From 1700 to 1716 Polhem worked at the copper mines in Falun. During this time he developed many inventions for the mining industry, such as pumps, water-powered hammers and his unusual linkage system for the transmission of mechanical power over distances via long reciprocating wooden bars. One such linkage system renowned for the boldness of its construction was set up at the Hundbo mine, where power was brought in over rough terrain from a water wheel located 2.5 km away.

Despite Polhem's successes, many of his contemporaries regarded his new-fangled creations with skepticism.

During his travels, Polhem found inspiration for exploiting some of the possibilities offered by Swedish industry. He established a foundry at Stjärnsund to be able to demonstrate these new ideas. The works at Stjärnsund manufactured special machines for woodworking, cutting gears, making files and, in particular, produced kitchen tools, looms, hardware and burglar-proof locks (the Polhem lock) as well as clocks.

Polhem was also interested in transportation. In 1717 he suggested building a canal between the cities of Norrköping and Gothenburg (the Svea Canal) which would unite Sweden's east and west coasts. Work was begun fairly soon thereafter, but was not completed until 1795, after many delays. Polhem was also hired for a number of other engineering projects, including the construction of sluices, bridges, sawmills and brickyards.

In addition to his varied technical accomplishments, Polhem engaged in an extensive correspondence in many other areas, such as economics, agriculture and navigation. He assisted in the establishment of Sweden's first society for experimentation in the natural sciences, the Collegium Curioserum in Uppsala.

ANDERS CELSIUS

Anders Celsius (1701–1744) exhibited unusual mathematical talent, even as a young schoolboy. He soon gave up the law studies he had begun at Uppsala University to devote himself entirely to mathematics and astronomy. He was appointed professor of astronomy at Uppsala University at the age of 29. Celsius' wish that an observatory be built in Uppsala resulted in Sweden's first observatory being erected there in 1741. The observatory was formally opened the following year and still stands today, with the exception of its upper section. As an astronomer, Celsius made countless observations and so contributed to world knowledge of solar and lunar eclipses, the orbits of the planets, comets, the aberrations of the stars, and the breakdown of light in the atmosphere.

Celsius is best remembered for his centigrade thermometer, which is used in many areas of the world today. In 1741 he first used his experimental thermometer, which is preserved at Uppsala University's Department of Meteorology. Initially, Celsius had placed the boiling point of water at zero degrees and the melting point of ice at one hundred degrees. It is said that it was Carl Linnaeus who reversed the scale.

Celsius' thermometer has gained widespread use because the boiling point of water and the melting point of ice are two reference points that are easy to identify and re-create.

CARL LINNAEUS

Carl Linnaeus (1707–1778), also known as von Linné, is best known for his system of classification for the plant, animal and mineral worlds published in his Systema Naturae. He undertook many scientific travels, which resulted in comprehensive written reports. The most famous of his travels were to Lapland in 1732, a province in northern Sweden, to the province of Dalarna in 1734 and his final trip to the province of Skåne in 1749. He sent his students to the far corners of the world to collect specimens and report on their findings. Pehr Osbeck, Anders Sparrman and Carl Peter Thunberg traveled to China, Sparrman and Daniel Solander participated in Captain James Cook's circumnavigation of the globe, and Thunberg visited Japan. Johan Peter Falck explored Inner Asia, Pehr Kalm traveled to North America, Roland Martin to the Polar Sea, Daniel Rolander and Pehr Löfling to South America, Fredrik Hasselqvist and Peter Forsskål to the Holy Land and Arabia.

Linnaeus' stature as a natural historian, especially as a botanist and medical doctor, was not fully appreciated until much later. Through his admonition to build upon experience only, Linnaeus struck a great blow for the natural sciences as inductive research. Even today, Linnaeus continues to hold a pivotal role in biology.

His two hundred year old collections continue to reveal secrets to modern scientists, although the plant specimens are beginning to fall apart after having been studied by several generations of botanists. While the greatest portion of Linnaeus' collections can be found at the Linnean Society in London, other parts of his collections exist in Sweden, Finland, France, Germany, Russia and Switzerland.

In order to preserve Linnaeus' research for posterity, his pressed flowers are being photographed with high-definition digital cameras and the images stored on CD-ROM. The Linnaeus collection in Moscow has already been photographed at a resolution of 700 points per inch, making it possible to study details as tiny as individual grains of pollen on a computer monitor.

As an indication of his importance, it is worth mentioning that Linnaeus' scientific works are some of the most often cited in the Science Citation Index.

PEHR WILHELM WARGENTIN

Pehr Wilhelm Wargentin (1717–1783), astronomer and statistician, combined scientific prowess with good organizational skills. In 1748 Wargentin was made a member of the Royal Swedish Academy of Sciences (KVA) and by a unanimous vote in 1749 he was appointed Secretary of the Academy. In this capacity, he contributed greatly to the organization's consolidation and favorable reputation.

In addition to his significant astronomical observations, Wargentin laid the foundations of Sweden's remarkable census statistics. This system began with a church law passed in 1686, which ruled that church records must be kept to provide information about births and deaths, as well as inward and outward migration between parishes. In 1749 Sweden's Bureau of Tables was established with Wargentin as its head. Here the statistical material from the churches was to be compiled. Thus Sweden (and Finland, which was part of Sweden at that time) was the first country in the world to maintain population statistics. The Bureau of Tables was reorganized in 1756 as the Commission of Tables and is known today as Statistics Sweden (SCB). An announcement authored by Wargentin in 1761 is considered to show the insight he had into the value statistics could hold for society. Wargentin produced numerous statistical works and his studies of mortality rates and life expectancies attracted widespread attention.

The work of Pehr Wargentin has meant much, not only for genealogists, but also for medical researchers, who have been able to map out inherited and other diseases thanks to Swedish population statistics.

EVA EKEBLAD

Eva Ekeblad (1724–1786), born de la Gardie, was one of Sweden's early female inventors. She experimented with potatoes for both the production of powder and the distillation of vodka. Her attempts to produce potato vodka succeeded in 1748, and the Swedes began to grow more potatoes for alcohol production. With time, the Swedes found the courage to try eating potatoes, too.

In reward for her invention, Eva Ekeblad was the first woman admitted to the Royal Swedish Academy of Sciences (KVA). This move was inspired by trends in countries outside Sweden, which had begun to admit women into their science academies. There was a desire in Sweden to show recognition and respect which would encourage "the entire gender to pay strict attention to each and every aspect of keeping of the household."

CARL WILHELM SCHEELE

Carl Wilhelm Scheele (1742–1786) began as a pharmacist's apprentice in Gothenburg. On his own he acquired such a vast knowledge of chemistry that he surpassed most of the internationally known chemists of the day and was admitted to the Royal Swedish Academy of Sciences (KVA) in 1775. In 1777 he passed the pharmacology exam. He was faithful to that profession until his death, by which time he was regarded as one of the greatest chemical scientists.

At the time of his death, no one had surpassed his record for the number of important discoveries. Scheele developed many excellent methods of analysis. He was primarily an experimental researcher, equipped with re-markable powers of observation, judgment, knowledge and ingenuity in regard to thinking through and carrying out experiments.

Scheele was the first to state that a specific type of metal could go through different stages of oxidation. He discovered nine basic elements, among them oxygen, chlorine and molybdenum. In addition he was the first to isolate a number of elements.

Scheele was unassuming, reticent, hard-working and totally absorbed by his scientific interests. His life was spent in a small-town milieu where his research, the management of his pharmacy and a scientific correspondence took up all of his time.

JÖNS JACOB BERZELIUS

Jöns Jacob Berzelius (1779–1848), a chemist, was one of the first to accept Dalton's atomic theory (of ca. 1803). Using the atomic theory and, among other things, Gay-Lussac's Law, he developed the first table of atomic weights, a comprehensive work published in 1818. He had measured the atomic weights of 45 of the 49 basic elements known to exist at that time and the values he found are surprisingly close to measurements made using modern methods.

Berzelius also introduced the simplified system of identifying the basic elements by one or two letters taken from their Latin names. Over time this language of symbols has come to be used by all chemists. In 1817 he discovered the element selenium, in 1823 silicon, and in 1828 thorium.

Berzelius also authored textbooks in Swedish which were in great demand, for example his Lectures in Biological Chemistry, 2 volumes, 1806–1808, and Textbook in Chemistry, 6 volumes, 1808–1830. These books have been translated into a number of languages.

Berzelius had a great capacity for work and did much of his research alone, without students or assistants. However, he cooperated with many Swedish and foreign chemists.

ANDERS JONAS ÅNGSTRÖM

Anders Jonas Ångström (1814–1874), physicist, mapped out a complete exploration of natural magnetic conditions in Sweden and determined the inclination and intensity of magnetic fields in a number of regions around the country. His program was a comprehensive one and the magnetic mapping of Sweden was not completed until 1934. However, Ångström's chief interests lay neither in geophysics nor thermology, but rather in optics, a pursuit which he followed throughout his life.

Ångström carried out a much-appreciated pioneering feat, which has been the basis for the entire field of modern spectroanalysis. He analyzed the basic elements of the sun, and in 1868 he published a map of the spectra of almost one hundred elements. Ångström was the first to measure wavelengths in absolute numbers. He introduced the basic unit of one ten millionth of a millimeter, which in 1905 was named the "angstrom" in his honor. ($1\text{ Å} = 0.1$ nm.)

INNOVATIONS FROM PRE-INDUSTRIAL SWEDEN

Beginning in the 1870s Swedish industry experienced an unprecedented period of expansion. Sweden's system of compulsory elementary education, which had been introduced in 1842, contributed greatly to increased reading and writing skills throughout the country and transformed Sweden from an agricultural nation to an industrial one. The following decades saw the establishment of many major corporations which would come to play huge roles in Swedish industry. Primarily these corporations produced engineering products, and they became so successful that their inventors and engineers became the heroes of their day. Many of these names are well known even today.

Sweden was a small nation in relation to its population and from their beginnings, these corporations were forced to look abroad. Good ideas and the capacity for precision manufacturing led to the powerful expansion of Swedish industry. In addition, many countries needed to be rebuilt after various wars from which Sweden had been spared. Building up Sweden's own military defense forces also contributed to industrial growth and provided an opportunity for the development and testing of new products. (Military inventions have not been included in this book since information about them is often difficult to obtain.)

Some of the corporations established during this period include Atlas Copco, Ericsson, ASEA (today known as ABB), Alfa Laval, Stal Laval, AGA, SKF, ESAB and Sandvik.

EARLY ON, ERICSSON FOCUSED ON EXPORTS. HERE AN ERICSSON TELEPHONE IS SEEN IN USE ON THE ISLAND OF JAVA IN THE EARLY 1900s.

ALFRED NOBEL

Alfred Nobel (1833–1896) was born in Stockholm, but at 9 years of age moved with his family to St. Petersburg in Russia. There, his father Immanuel, an engineer and inventor, had set up a workshop to manufacture anti-personnel mines for the Russian army. St. Petersburg was at that time a great European metropolis renowned for being rich in cultural offerings, and for its lively scientific activity and a sparkling society life. The Nobel boys were instructed by leading university professors rather than going to school. Their education embraced both the humanities and the natural sciences. In addition to Swedish, Alfred and his brothers were taught Russian, French, English and German, and they studied literature and philosophy as well.

Alfred Nobel—inventor, industrialist and humanist—produced many inventions. He received a total of 355 patents during his lifetime, the most significant of which were in the field of explosives.

NOBEL INNOVATIONS

DETONATOR CAP While still in St. Petersburg, Nobel worked with the production and use of nitroglycerine. Returning to Stockholm in 1864, Nobel was at 31 years of age granted a patent for his detonator cap for nitroglycerine, a revolutionary invention which made it possible to use nitroglycerine as an explosive. The demand for this volatile "blasting oil" meant that huge volumes had to be produced. That same year Nobel's nitroglycerine factory at Heleneborg Manor in the Södermalm district of Stockholm was destroyed as the result of an explosion. The accident claimed five lives, including Emil Oscar Nobel, the youngest of the Nobel brothers. Alfred Nobel continued developing the production methods for nitroglycerine and the design of his detonator in order to achieve more effective and safer production and use of this explosive.

DYNAMITE Alfred Nobel continued to experiment with various compositions in order to stabilize his explosive "oil." The solution proved to be kieselguhr, a special type of sand. In 1866 he introduced "Nobel's Safety Explosive"—dynamite. The blasting of the St. Gotthard Tunnel, the New York City subways, the Panama Canal—to mention but a few projects—made the name Nobel world-famous.

GELIGNITE Nobel continued with his research and development and in 1875 he introduced a new explosive called blasting gelatin. This compound consists of 93% nitroglycerine and 7% collodium, a form of gun cotton (nitrocellulose) dissolved in ether. Blasting gelatin thus combines two active components in a stable, safe manner. It is more powerful than nitroglycerine and can be used for blasting under water.

BALLISTITE A few years later, Nobel invented a smokeless powder based on nitroglycerine, with greater explosive force than black powder. Ballistite revolutionized military munitions technology.

ARTIFICIAL MATERIALS Nobel pursued many research projects simultaneously. His work on the development of dynamite was the beginning of an entire "family" of artificial materials. Working on his own between 1876 and 1890 he developed production methods for artificial rubber and synthetic leather, using nitrocellulose as the basic ingredient.

In 1894, he obtained a comprehensive patent describing the use of nitrocellulose for making artificial leather, synthetic rubber, thread, lacquers and varnishes. Many feel that this was one of Nobel's most futuristic patents. It was not until the 1920s that other synthetic lacquers and varnishes came onto the market.

In 1892 Nobel was contacted by Robert Strehlenert, a Swedish chemist who had an idea which captured Nobel's interest. Strehlenert wanted to produce artificial silk from nitrocellulose. Their collaboration was highly successful and Strehlenert began the spinning of artificial silk on a laboratory basis. Cooperative work between the two continued for as long as Nobel lived.

THE NOBEL PRIZES

Alfred Nobel's fortune can be attributed to his ability to combine the qualities of scientist and inventor with those of a visionary industrialist. Nobel's corporations were founded upon his many patents. He owned 90 factories in 20 countries. Their production rose from 11 metric tons in 1867 to 60,000 metric tons by 1895. Nobel's personal fortune was estimated to have been just over SEK 30 million. In his will, Nobel stipulated that the major part of his estate was to be converted into a foundation and invested in "safe" securities. Accordingly, SEK 31.5 million (equivalent to some SEK 1.5 billion in 2002) was used to establish the Nobel Foundation.

Nobel announced that the interest on the rest of his entire estate was to be distributed "in the form of prizes to those who, during the preceding year, have conferred the greatest benefit on mankind" in the fields of physics, chemistry, physiology or medicine, literature and work for the promotion of peace.

At its tercentenary in 1968, the Sveriges Riksbank instituted the Bank of Sweden Prize in Economic Sciences in Memory of Alfred Nobel, pledging an annual amount to the Nobel Foundation equal to one of the regular Nobel Prizes.

Alfred Nobel's will drew attention from around the world. It was not common to donate such large sums of money to scientific and philanthropic causes. Many criticized the international nature of the prizes and felt that they should have been reserved for Swedes, but this would not have suited a cosmopolitan like Alfred Nobel. Some family members contested the will and a series of legal and administrative complications had to be settled. This proved a lengthy procedure, but eventually all was resolved and the first Nobel Prizes could be awarded in 1901.

The awards are widely recognized as the world's highest civil honors. Besides spurring recipients and potential candidates to new efforts in their disciplines, they play a valuable role in publicizing scientific and literary achievements and humanitarian endeavors throughout the world.

LEFT: THE NOBEL CENTENNIAL PRIZE CEREMONY HELD AT THE STOCKHOLM CONCERT HALL, ON DECEMBER 10, 2001.
TOP: THE MEDAL FOR PHYSICS AND CHEMISTRY.

SAFETY MATCH

Gustaf Erik Pasch (1788–1862), Johan Edvard Lundström (1815–1888), and Alexander Lagerman (1836–1904) laid the groundwork for the Swedish match industry.

In 1844 Pasch received a patent for the safety match, in which the deadly yellow phosphorus used in earlier matches was replaced with red phosphorus, which he placed in the striking surface of the matchbox rather than in the head of the match. Johan Edvard Lundström

and his brother, Carl Frans Lundström (1823–1917), who established the Jönköping Match Factory in 1844–1845, adopted Pasch's invention and improved it.

In 1855 J.E. Lundström was granted a patent for a completely phosphorus-free match, which was put into production in 1857. Safety matches were more expensive than phosphorus matches.

MATCH MACHINE

In 1864 Alexander Lagerman at 28 years of age constructed the first automatic match-making machine. It was developed into a practical form in 1892, making possible the mass production of matches.

The "complete process machine" which Lagerman developed made both matches and matchboxes, and it produced filled matchboxes ready for sale. In 1898 Lagerman's match machine had a production capacity of 40,000 boxes of matches per day. (Lagerman also developed the platen printing press, which had a huge effect upon the printing industry and was an economic success.

This printing press was Lagerman's last invention before he died in 1904.)

The manufacture of matches became the basis for a huge corporate empire led by industrialist Ivar Kreuger (1880–1932). At one point Swedish corporations had a monopoly on world match production, accounting for 75% of all matches manufactured worldwide. After Kreuger died in Paris in 1932, it took ten years to complete the legal examination into the bankruptcy which followed his death. By that time, only a fraction of his huge empire remained.

SCREW PROPELLER

As a 20-year old, John Ericsson (1803–1889) devoted all his free time to his inventions, among which was a hot-air engine. In 1826, unable to find anyone to finance his engine, he traveled to the UK. There he had difficulty getting the engine to work properly because the heat produced by English coal was too intense. Ericsson shifted his focus and produced a new type of steam boiler, the "tube boiler," which he used in constructing his "Novelty" locomotive, which competed against George Stephenson's "Rocket." Ericsson's locomotive was faster, but due to damage it could not compete in the final, decisive stage of the contest.

Ericsson's many developments included hot-air and steam engines and solar heaters, but his most important work as an inventor was in the area of propellers for ships. While Ericsson was not the first to construct a propeller, his design for driving ships was the first practical one. Propellers have barely changed in appearance since Ericsson presented his design.

Following his successes with propeller design and innovative steam engines, Ericsson focused once again upon the construction of hot-air engines. He made significant progress and in 1865 he received a patent for a small, easily-maintained machine which could operate on different types of fuel. The engine was a success and made Ericsson financially independent.

Ericsson gained his greatest fame for building the Monitor, the Union Navy's armored warship which conquered the Confederate navy's Merrimac during the American Civil War. The Monitor was 52 meters long, 12 meters wide and clad entirely in plate iron. Of the Monitor only the deck, two canons in a rotating gun turret, the command bridge and the smokestacks were visible above the surface of the water. The ship was completed on January 30, 1862 and on March 4, the battle between the Merrimac (armed with ten fixed guns all around) and Ericsson's Monitor took place at Hampton Roads in Chesapeake Bay. The Merrimac was unable to damage the smaller ship and was forced to retreat. The success of the Monitor was a contributing factor to the establishment of the Union navy's dominance at sea.

Over 100 warships were built using this design, including four for the Swedish navy. The only well-preserved Monitor-type ship in the world is the Sölve, which can be seen today at the Maritime Museum in Gothenburg.

THE CREAM SEPARATOR WAS THE FIRST TRULY SUCCESSFUL EXPORT PRODUCT FOR SWEDEN'S YOUNG INDUSTRIAL SECTOR.

CREAM SEPARATOR

In 1872, after working and studying in both Sweden and Germany, Gustaf de Laval (1845–1913) devoted himself to what would become his most important invention, the cream separator. He began work on his design after having studied the centrifugal separator developed by Wilhelm Lefeldt of Germany. De Laval immediately realized the importance of rapid revolving action and he designed a machine that revolved several times faster than Lefeldt's.

In 1877, de Laval left for Stockholm, where he continued to experiment with the famous cream separator which bore his name. The first model was patented in 1878, and 1883 saw the establishment of the Separator company (today Alfa-Laval).

De Laval designed other apparatuses for the dairy industry, including a milking machine. Yet one of his greatest inventions was a steam turbine with a spring-cushioned shaft which he introduced in 1892. It was a clear improvement over existing designs.

This turbine was equipped with specially-shaped steam jets, "Laval jets," which gave the steam a speed greater than the speed of sound when it hit the turbine blades. De Laval's innovative shaft and steam jet designs meant that his turbine produced extremely high speeds, between 10,000 and 40,000 rpm, with high efficiency. De Laval's steam turbine represented a significant improvement in steam efficiency. During the 1900s, it was the most-widely used steam power source in the world.

De Laval was renowned for his considerable talent and versatility and unfailing enthusiasm. In the 1890s his research workshop employed over 100 engineers and he produced thousands of new ideas for inventions. However, de Laval was often happy to merely develop the basic idea and leave the practical details to others.

TELEPHONE HANDSET

Lars Magnus Ericsson (1846–1926) was trained as a blacksmith. In 1872 he was granted a travel scholarship to Germany and Switzerland, where, between 1872 and 1876, he studied primarily electrical engineering. After his time abroad Ericsson opened a precision instrument workshop, L.M. Ericsson & Co. Ericsson showed great talent both as a technician and as a shop manager. He began manufacturing telephones in 1878 and his first telephone was released on the market in 1881. In the same year he delivered the first central switchboard for 50 lines to the city of Norrköping in central Sweden. The following years saw new designs and product deliveries one after the other. The first telephones in Sweden had been manufactured abroad, but Ericsson's telephones soon dominated the Swedish market.

The first automatic telephone switchboards in Sweden, developed by Ericsson and a jeweller named Henrik Cedergren (1853–1909), were introduced as early as 1886. The Stockholm Public Telephone Company, founded by Cedergren in 1883, made use of Ericsson's technology, and as a result, Stockholm had more telephones per capita than any other city in the world in 1885.

Early on, the Ericsson Company focused on exports, especially to Russia, Finland, Norway, Denmark, the Netherlands and the UK. Ericsson factories were established outside Sweden and many Ericsson telephone exchanges were built around the world. Although Ericsson was primarily a great corporate leader, he also made a number of improvements to the telephones of the era, as well as developing switchboards and laying telephone networks. In 1885 he invented the telephone handset.

In the 1890s, when the company's technological advances drew international attention, L.M. Ericsson established a number of subsidiary companies outside Sweden. In 1903 Ericsson gave up active leadership in his company, which had become a genuine multinational. By that point of time his factories had manufactured over 400,000 telephones and other types of equipment.

ADJUSTABLE WRENCH

Johan Petter Johansson (1853–1943) began inventing when he was very young. He started his own company in 1886 after having worked in various technical fields. In his work as a fitter, he and his assistants often had to carry numerous wrenches for various screws and nuts. He invented the "universal wrench" (an adjustable pipe wrench) in 1888, and in 1892 he constructed and patented the first adjustable nut wrench. Altogether, J.P. Johansson produced 118 inventions. Many of them were used around the world and are still manufactured today.

J.P. Johansson had made the move from repairman to constructor and manufacturer. He established and led his own company until 1914, when he sold the majority of the stock to B.A. Hjort & Co., a subsidiary of Bahco. Sandvik Bahco has manufactured over 100 million adjustable wrenches, and production continues. Each year, about 40 million adjustable wrenches are manufactured around the world using the design developed by Johan Petter Johansson.

Another of Johansson's inventions was the Triplex lamp. This adjustable lamp, which he finished in 1919, was a predecessor to the adjustable table-mounted work lamps seen today. That same year Johansson started the Triplex factory, which he managed until his death in 1943.

THREE-PHASE ELECTRICAL SYSTEM

Jonas Wenström (1855–1893) was an electrician and inventor. He had considerable knowledge of physics and related fields, which he broadened during extensive study trips. From the late 1870s onward, he devoted himself to the study of various areas of electrical research, primarily electrotechnology.

He turned over his first inventions to industrialist Ludvig Fredholm, and with Fredholm as general manager he founded Sweden's first electrical company, Elektriska AB in Stockholm. In 1890 Wenström became chief engineer at Allmänna Svenska Elektriska AB (ASEA, today ABB). There he continued his diverse and successful career as an inventor, developing numerous direct-current machines and more. Among other things, he designed an electric locomotive. With government grants he visited Germany and Switzerland, where he found new inspiration for his ideas concerning power transmission.

Wenström's most important contributions were his theoretical examinations, which led to the invention of the three-phase electrical system. Together with the inventor Nicolai Tesla he is honored as the father of alternating current (according to the courts, Wenström was first). Wenström's patent of 1891 covered the entire system for the transmission of power in the form of three-phase electrical current. It also included the machines necessary for the use of this system—generators, transformers and motors.

Wenström developed many electrical inventions, and his direct-current generator is a classic. His inventions became the basis for ASEA, which was formed thanks to royalties Wenström received for his patented three-phase electrical system.

In 1892 the first practical three-phase motor was constructed in Sweden and in 1893 the validity of Wenström's theories was proven when an ASEA-built hydroelectric power station was completed in the province of Dalarna. Electrical power equal to 300 horsepower was transferred from the facility at Hällsjön to the mining operations at Grängesberg, a distance of 15 km. This was the beginning of the electrification of Sweden.

THE ASEA-BUILT HYDROELECTRIC POWER STATION AT HELLSJÖN IN THE PROVINCE OF DALARNA.

27

BLOWTORCH

Carl Richard Nyberg (1858–1939) was an inventor and industrialist. Upon completing elementary school, Nyberg worked for a goldsmith. In 1874 he came to Stockholm and in 1881 he began working at J.E. Eriksson's factory, which manufactured petroleum stoves. His eagerness to increase their efficiency soon gave him an idea for a new sort of soldering torch.

In 1881 Nyberg invented the blowtorch and by 1882 he had developed his idea into practical form. He began production in a former laundry room, but moved to another facility a few years later. The Nyberg blowtorch operated on kerosene in much the same manner as a kerosene stove: by air pressure the kerosene is forced through a jet, where it is heated and vaporized. The vaporized kerosene is then ignited and burned together with large quantities of air.

The blowtorch was small and convenient and many tradesmen used it daily, because it easily provided high heat for many different purposes. Only during the last 20 years has the kerosene-burning blowtorch been outperformed by liquid-gas torches. Thus Nyberg's blowtorch had a lifetime of about 100 years.

Nyberg's blowtorch was used around the world. Its economic success allowed him to pursue an idea which he had been interested in earlier, namely aircraft. As early as 1878 he built several models of a screw-shaped aircraft, but in 1897 he turned to a more conventional design using the principle of wings and a propeller. Nyberg is considered a pioneer in this area. The combustion engine had not yet been developed and, despite a series of experiments with lightweight steam engines, Nyberg never succeeded in constructing an aircraft light enough to lift off. Yet through his experiments Nyberg made a number of discoveries which were later put to use in aircraft technology. One of these concerned laws regarding air resistance on wings and propellers at different speeds, which Nyberg had worked out in a wind tunnel he had constructed.

ZIPPER

The zipper was developed in 1900 by Gideon Sundbäck (1880–1954). A number of different zip-type fasteners had been invented since the 1800s, but the first design to function satisfactorily was Sundbäck's.

The patent for the modern zipper design, that is two woven cotton bands with metal teeth and a pull which could join or separate the teeth, was granted in 1914 in the USA.

By the time the patent was granted, Sundbäck had emigrated to the USA, where he established a factory for the production of his invention.

The appearance of the zipper has not changed since Sundbäck's day. The only change occurred in the 1970s when the metal teeth were replaced by plastic, and this newer version has not proven to be as dependable or long-lasting. Other attempts to replace zippers with Velcro have not met with great success. Even today the majority of zippers are made of cotton and metal.

SWEDISH INNOVATIONS
1900-1950

COMBINATION GAUGE

Carl Edvard Johansson's (1864–1943) greatest achievement was developing and then receiving international recognition for his methods for the precision measurement and inspection of machine components. He also succeeded in introducing a simple, unified set of relational measures between imperial and metric units of measure. Johansson's new systems came at a time when the need for precision measurement was on the increase, and such measurements were crucial to the mass production of engineering products and the establishment of Sweden's corporate industries. C.E. Johansson found that, in theory, a combination gauge consisting of 120 gauge blocks could accommodate all measurements between 1 mm and 201 mm in consistent increments with a variance of 0.01 mm, a total of 20,000 measurements in all.

While working at a rifle factory in the town of Eskilstuna, Johansson discovered that the gauge blocks used there did not provide sufficiently precise measurements. This was the beginning of his endeavors between 1897 and 1906 to build gauge blocks of greater precision—his combination gauges. His work generated considerable interest in the engineering industry, and in 1910 he established his firm, C.E. Johansson & Co., which one year later was reorganized as AB C.E. Johansson. The gauges he introduced in 1901 had a tolerance of one thousandth of a millimeter, and in 1907 he applied for a patent for a gauge for even closer tolerances.

"Precision Johansson's" measuring blocks played an important role in the engineering industry, both in Sweden and abroad, especially in the American automobile industry. For a time C.E. Johansson worked for Henry Ford.

AGA LIGHTHOUSE

Following technical studies in Gothenburg and Zurich, inventor and industrialist Gustaf Dalén (1869–1937) pursued an interest in acetylene gas.

During the years 1905–1909, Dalén developed four famous inventions which became the cornerstones of the AGA system: 1) aga, a gas storage medium which reduced the risk of acetylene explosions during transport, 2) an intermittent lamp (1905) for lighthouses which gave rapid flashes of light from acetylene gas, 3) his solar valve (1907), which automatically lit the gas lamp of a lighthouse when darkness fell and extinguished it at daybreak and 4) the Dalén mixer (1909), an apparatus which blended acetylene gas with air. The first installation of the AGA system for lighthouse illumination was completed already in 1904. AGA lighthouses became virtually maintenance-free when Dalén added a device which automatically changed burned-out gas mantles.

These lighthouses brought huge savings in personnel and material costs and increased the safety of ocean transport. Dalén's lighthouse system was used around the world during most of the 20th century. His system was also used in other applications such as lighted buoys, aircraft landing lights, wind indicators and railroad signals. In 1906 he became a chief engineer with the Swedish Gas Accumulator Company, and he later served as vice president of the same company. In 1912 Dalén was blinded in a gas accumulator accident. Despite his misfortune he continued as vice president of AGA until just before his death.

Under Dalén's leadership AGA developed into a multinational company with sales organizations in most countries. Another of his inventions was the AGA cooker in 1929. This popular cooking stove, which burns coke, is manufactured by a foreign company today.

In 1912 Gustaf Dalén was awarded the Nobel Prize in Physics.

THE LJUNGSTRÖM TURBINE WAS AN INSTANT SUCCESS. AMONG OTHER APPLICATIONS, IT POWERED THE STREETCARS OF LONDON.

LJUNGSTRÖM TURBINE

Birger Ljungström (1872–1948) and his brother Fredrik Ljungström (1875–1964) began their inventing early. When only 23 years old, Birger Ljungström introduced the Svea Velocipede, a bicycle with adjustable gears, freewheeling and a foot brake—an invention which attracted much attention in its day. The Svea's pedals worked up-and-down rather than in a circular motion. A factory to manufacture this new creation was established in the UK with financial help from Alfred Nobel. Unfortunately the enterprise was never a success and ended up being liquidated.

The brothers had a number of other renowned creations, the most famous of which was the Ljungström turbine. The first sketch was made and patented in 1894 and production began in 1908 with the founding of the Ljungström Steam Turbine Company. The new turbine was an instant success. Among other applications, it powered the streetcars of London.

The Ljungström turbine is a radial turbine, that is, the steam is directed from the center of the turbine blade out to the periphery. The turbine lacked fixed vanes. Instead, the blades were shaped so that they also served as vanes for the outer turbine blade. The Ljungström turbine had two shafts which rotated in opposite directions. For this reason it was often referred to as the double rotation turbine.

One of Fredrik Ljungström's most important inventions was an air preheater. This rotating heat exchanger increases the efficiency of steam boilers by recycling heat from exhaust gases to warm the incoming air supply. More than 20,000 of these preheaters have been installed around the world and they are still manufactured by Svenska Rotor Machines of Stockholm. While the Ljungström preheater is not generally listed as one of the most famous Swedish inventions, it was honored in 1995 by the American Society of Mechanical Engineers (ASME) as one of the greatest mechanical inventions ever, and was elevated to the status of an "International Historical Mechanical Engineering Landmark."

Also well known is the Ljungström boat, a sailboat with a boomless, rotating mast. The boat has a single "double" sail that can be unfolded in favorable winds. Another Ljungström invention was a method for the extraction of shale oil, which was of considerable importance for Sweden's fuel supply during the lean years of the 1940s.

THE MODEL 4 VACUUM CLEANER LAUNCHED BY ELECTROLUX IN 1919.

HOUSEHOLD VACUUM CLEANER

The first electric vacuum cleaner was invented around 1880 in the USA. It was a large machine equipped with bellows and crankshafts, which made it difficult to use. However, the trend was toward smaller, easier-to-use vacuum cleaners, and in 1910 Eberhard Seger (1854–1923) constructed a smaller machine for home use.

Seger established the Salus factory to manufacture his vacuum cleaners. He also collaborated with the Lux company, which later was merged in Electrolux, and in 1912 the first production series vacuum cleaners came out on the market.

Vacuum cleaners were constantly undergoing improvements. In 1913 Lux received initial patents. The company finally received its first patent for an entire vacuum cleaner in 1915. This model had an electrically-driven fan which drew the dust in through a nozzle fixed to the end of a flexible hose, into a dust collection bag made of cloth (much like the vacuum cleaners of today). This machine weighed only 19 kg and took up very little space, which made it easy to use in the home.

Vacuum cleaners were soon widely accepted, and today they are part of the standard equipment for a home. Vacuum cleaners are still one of the major products of the Electrolux company.

PRIMUS STOVE

Frans Wilhelm Lindqvist (1862–1931), an inventor and industrialist, began working in the metal refining industry in the town of Eskilstuna. He moved on to Gothenburg and then Stockholm, where after a while he found work in the shops of the Separator company. There, together with his brother Carl Anders Lindqvist, he developed the kerosene stove, which they patented in 1891.

Before Lindqvist created his stove, kerosene-fired stoves had worked on the same principle as a kerosene lamp, that is using a wick and an open flame. Lindqvist hit upon the idea of preheating the kerosene so that it was vaporized before burning. This made for a stove that provided much more heat and which did not smoke. Together with machine shop owner Johan V. Svensson he began to manufacture the new stove, which he dubbed the Primus. In 1898 the company was merged into AB Primus. During the period 1905–1918 Lindqvist served as vice president of the corporation, which at times had as many as 700 employees.

The Primus stove was a huge success and was exported all over the world. Around 50 million of them were produced by a number of different manufacturers and they were also sold under other names such as the Radius Stove, the Svea Stove and the Optimus Stove. These kerosene stoves are still an important piece of equipment for many Bedouins on the move in deserts, and many modern day campers still use Primus stoves. The Swedish marketing genius B.A. Hjort contributed greatly to the huge success of the Primus stove and to J.P. Johansson's adjustable wrench—two products for which he held the world sales rights. In 1918 Lindqvist sold his share in Primus to B.A. Hjort & Co. Upon his death in 1931 he bequeathed SEK 1 million to the cause of needy elderly persons in Stockholm.

IN THE 1930s, ELECTROLUX BEGAN EMPLOYING WORLD-FAMOUS DESIGNERS SUCH AS RAYMOND LOEWY AND SIXTEN SASON FOR THE DESIGN OF SOME OF ITS APPLIANCES. THIS REFRIGERATOR FROM 1938 WAS DESIGNED BY RAYMOND LOEWY.

REFRIGERATOR WITHOUT MOVING PARTS

The first functional household refrigerator, the Domeir, was manufactured in Chicago in 1913. A dozen more brand names appeared on the American market in the years leading up to 1916. Most of these refrigerators consisted of two separate units: an insulated container holding cooling tubes and a refrigeration unit, which was often located in the cellar. The refrigeration unit used sulfurous acid as a cooling agent.

The invention of a refrigerator without moving parts was a revolution. Swedish engineers Baltzar von Platen (1898–1984) and Carl Munters (1897–1989) succeeded in "generating cold by using heat." The cold was produced in a sealed system in which a cooling agent (ammonia) was vaporized (boiled) by heat. The ammonia vapor was absorbed by water and pumped back into the vaporizer. This invention drew great interest both in Sweden and abroad. Albert Einstein was very impressed by the work of these two men and their theoretical solution for the generation of cold temperatures.

Production and sales began in 1925, paving the way for the corporation that would become Electrolux. At last there was a way to store fresh food. By 1930 prices dropped as the refrigerators became more and more common. That year the national housing cooperative HSB made the refrigerator a standard item in its apartments.

In 1926 the General Electric company in the USA began manufacturing hermetically sealed compressor units, and in 1939 the first refrigerator with two temperature levels was introduced, making it possible to keep frozen foods in a special freezer compartment.

Carl Munters remained at Electrolux until 1936. He continued as an inventor and devoted himself to heating and cooling problems. As early as the 1930s he developed a form of foam plastic. Some of his very successful later inventions include dehumidifying units, air conditioners, air scrubbers, cooling towers, heat exchangers and water purification plants.

Carl Munters died in 1989 at 92 years of age. During his lifetime he was granted patents for more than a thousand of his own inventions.

ULTRACENTRIFUGE

Theodor "The" Svedberg (1884–1971), physical chemist, performed research on the characteristics of colloids. Researchers under Svedberg's leadership developed an elegant method of determining the size of particles in "rough dispersion" systems, that is, colloidal solutions with relatively large particles. The method was based upon the sedimentation of the particles caused by gravity. The smaller the particle, the slower it sinks. In order to use this method the weight of the particles had to be increased many times over, which Svedberg's team achieved through the use of a centrifuge.

The work began in 1922 and in 1924 Svedberg presented his method for determining of molecular weights using his "ultracentrifuge," which created the equivalent of 7,000 times the force of gravity. In 1925 a centrifuge was built in Uppsala, from which Svedberg obtained the equivalent of 100,000 times the force of gravity. This method is based upon the fact that molecules of different sizes and weights settle at different speeds in a gravitational field.

Ultracentrifuges have been improved over the years, and today they achieve gravitational forces 900,000–1,000,000 times that of the earth's. Under these circumstances one gram may have the same effect as a ton.

The molecular weight of complicated protein molecules can now be determined by measuring the speed at which large molecules settle under the influence of a gravitational field of known intensity. Modern ultracentrifuges make it possible to determine the weight of a molecule with an uncertainty of less than one percent. For his work regarding dispersion systems Theodore Svedberg received the Nobel Prize in Chemistry in 1926.

HASSELBLAD CAMERA

Hasselblad's history as a camera maker goes back to 1941, when the Viktor Hasselblad company was formed. The company manufactured aerial cameras for the Swedish air force. Viktor Hasselblad (1906–1978) also wanted to build a precision camera for civilian use. He envisioned a system of interchangeable lenses, film magazines and viewfinders. After six years of work he presented his camera, based on a single-lens reflex system.

Upon its debut in New York in 1948 the camera became a sensation. It used an image format of 6 cm x 6 cm, unlike earlier system-based cameras, which made use of tiny images. The media paid great attention to the Hasselblad when it became the first camera to take pictures in space in 1962. One of Hasselblad's greatest PR successes came later when his cameras were used on the American moon missions. After a Hasselblad camera was used to record Neil Armstrong and Buzz Aldrin's historic moonwalk in 1969, Hasselblad became one of the most recognized trademarks in the world. Since its introduction in 1948, Hasselblad's camera has undergone many improvements, and Hasselblad remains a dominant camera manufacturer. The Viktor Hasselblad Company has had several different owners in later years.

In his will Hasselblad donated SEK 78 million to the Erna and Viktor Hasselblad Research Foundation. Each year since 1980 the Foundation has awarded the Hasselblad Prize, one of the most prestigious photographic prizes in the world. The Prize consists of a gold medal and a monetary award.

LEFT: APOLLO 11 ASTRONAUT EDWIN E. "BUZZ" ALDRIN, JR. ON THE SURFACE OF THE MOON, A PHOTO TAKEN ON JULY 20, 1969, BY FELLOW ASTRONAUT AND FIRST MAN ON THE MOON, NEIL ARMSTRONG, USING A HASSELBLAD CAMERA. TOP: THE WELL-KNOWN DESIGN OF THE HASSELBLAD CAMERA. THE FIRST VERSION IN 1948 WAS DESIGNED BY SIXTEN SASON.

THE SPHERICAL BALL BEARING. TOP RIGHT: INVENTOR SVEN WINGQUIST AND A DRAFT OF HIS ORIGINAL DRAWINGS.

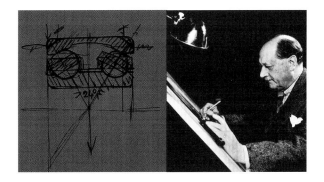

SPHERICAL ROLLER BEARING

Bearings have been crucial to the development of machine technology. While ball bearings have been used since the middle ages, Swedish inventor and industrialist Sven Wingquist (1876–1953) is regarded as the inventor of the modern roller bearing. In 1907 he invented the spherical ball bearing. Swedish industry has played a significant part in the development of roller bearings, particularly Svenska Kullager Fabriken, or as it is known internationally, SKF, the company founded by Sven Wingquist.

Railway and streetcar technology offered a very interesting field of application for bearing research. In 1923 the Swedish State Railways, accepted spherical, radial roller bearings for use in its railway cars.

C-BEARING The most often-used spherical roller bearing, the C-bearing (1948), was invented by Arvid Palmgren of SKF. Unlike earlier roller bearings the C-bearing had symmetrical rollers which were of equal thickness at both ends. In addition the C-bearing had a loose separator or cage which kept the rollers on the right course.

One advantage of the C-bearing is that it can withstand axial twisting, such as when a car drives around a curve. A bearing with symmetrical rollers maintains an even load on the rollers, even during axial twisting. When the bearing encounters twisting the outer ring moves axially in relation to the inner ring. Unlike older fixed separators the loose separator moves with the rollers as they adapt to the axial twisting without increasing the tension or friction on the ends of the rollers. Thus the C-bearing is able to carry a heavier load than earlier bearings, even when twisted.

CC-BEARING The CC-bearing (1972), a self-aligning roller bearing which greatly reduces friction against the flanges, was invented by engineers Magnus Kellström and Leif Blomqvist at SKF in Gothenburg. The CC-bearing produces lower friction values over a smaller area of distribution. Lower friction provides lower operating temperatures, so that the bearing requires less frequent lubrication and offers higher speeds and a longer life.

AXLELESS WHEEL BEARING In 1972 SKF introduced a completely new wheel bearing for automobiles which made axles unnecessary. The inventor was Sture Åberg. This bearing consists of a double-row angular contact bearing and is especially well adapted to front-wheel drive vehicles. It is low in both weight and cost. With an axleless bearing the number of components is drastically reduced, which means lower costs for both the bearings themselves and for vehicle assembly.

CARB™ BEARING The CARB™ bearing (Compact Aligning Roller Bearing) is a "new" roller bearing developed by Magnus Kellström. It combines the best of other types of bearings, can withstand greater axial forces and sideways thrust, and can carry heavier loads.

SWEDISH INNOVATIONS SINCE 1950

HIGH-VOLTAGE DIRECT CURRENT

Electricity must often be transported over long distances. For example, electricity is produced in northern Sweden and used mainly in the southern portion of the country. Such long transport distances lead to energy losses. These losses are reduced when higher voltage and direct current are used.

The method for the transmission of high-voltage direct current (HVDC) was developed by ASEA under the direction of Uno Lamm (1904–1989) during the 1930s. The development took several years and consisted of many partial solutions which were patented. In 1943 an important collaborative effort was undertaken by ASEA and Vattenfall, Sweden's then state-operated power company. The project involved high-tension direct current transmission between the western Swedish town of Trollhättan and Mellerud.

Similar developmental projects that had been undertaken in other countries were stopped by the Second World War, and by the time the war had come to an end, the projects had been abandoned. ASEA alone continued in these efforts, and the experiments at Trollhättan showed such promising results that in 1950 Vattenfall ordered a direct current transmission system between the Swedish mainland and the Swedish island of Gotland in the Baltic Sea. This system was used on a large scale for the first time in 1954. It is interesting to note that only a single cable had to be laid—the seawater itself served as the other conductor. The Gotland cable has been followed by a number of successors, including at Öresund between Sweden and Denmark, in Japan, the English Channel and in Canada.

In 1965 ASEA began an initiative that set the development of thyristor semiconductors in motion. In 1967 a switching station equipped with thyristors was installed as part of the Gotland power transmission project. Three years later ASEA was able to make the first commercial delivery of thyristor switching devices for HVDC.

ASEA Brown Boveri (ABB) has continued to develop the transmission of high-voltage direct current. Recently, the company introduced a method for the transmission of power from offshore and other distantly-located windpower farms called HVDC Light. In this system, the cables are buried deep under the earth. The first installation of HVDC Light was made on Gotland for the transmission of power from Näsudden to the town of Visby.

LEFT: THYRISTOR VALVE HALL IN DADRI, INDIA, PART OF THE RIHAND-DELHI HVDC POWER TRANSMISSION PLANT.

TETRA PAK

Tetra Pak in 1951 presented the revolutionizing idea for the storage of non-carbonated drinks such as milk and juice in plastic-coated paper containers. The inventors were Erik Wallenberg (1915–1999) and Ruben Rausing (1895–1983). Ruben Rausing had got his idea from the USA where milk was sold in containers made of wax-coated paper. Rausing, who thought this was too expensive, wanted to see an inexpensive and hygienic disposable container of paper.

In 1944 Erik Wallenberg hit upon the idea of a tetrahedron shape. A cylinder of plastic-coated paper was closed at both ends by two pressed seams located at right angles to one another. The resulting tetrahedron shape was well-suited to stacking and storage.

This development began at the firm of Åkerlund & Rausing in 1944, and really gained momentum in the newly-founded Tetra Pak in 1951. Tetra Pak built machines which could fill plastic-coated cartons with cream and milk on a continuous basis. The next stage was a re-shaping of the cartons to a more easily-handled square container. Later, a system for the aseptic handling of milk was developed. When Tetra Pak cartons were released on the market, they offerered consumers a simpler and more convenient way to handle milk for home use.

The development of this technology and the sale of cartons by vending machine was first adopted by the Swedish dairy industry in 1952, and by the end of the 1960s Tetra Pak products were in use throughout the world. Tetra Pak made new advances in packaging technology, for example their "Tetra Brik" carton was introduced in 1963. The company continuously developed its production machines and found new areas of application for its technologies.

Tetra Pak reached its stride as a corporation in the middle of the 1960s. The company continues to grow, and in 2001 Tetra Pak was reporting net sales of SEK 69.2 billion. That same year 94.1 billion cartons were delivered.

THE FIRST KNOWN SYNTHETIC DIAMONDS WERE PRODUCED IN 1953 BY ASEA.

QUINTUS PRESS

Baltzar von Platen (1898–1984) was the co-inventor of the refrigerator without moving parts during the 1920s (see p. 37). Toward the end of the 1930s, von Platen developed a high-pressure machine press with a large table area for use in the production of synthetic diamonds.

Around 1930 he had seen a diagram which showed the relationship between pressure and temperature when coal is crystallized into diamond. It was believed that it would be impossible to build a machine which could create the extremes of pressure and temperature necessary to duplicate this process. Nonetheless, von Platen took on the challenge and ASEA became interested in the project.

By 1950 Baltzar von Platen had developed a "diamond machine" which was further refined by ASEA, and in 1953 ASEA produced the first known synthetic diamond. The process used pressures of up to 80,000 atmospheres and temperatures of 1700 to 1800°C.

ASEA developed a series of high-pressure presses called the "Quintus press" for use in various applications. The Quintus press uses wire wound under tension around the frame of the press. Two of the engineers who worked on the development and application of the press were Hans Larker and Erik Lundblad. Even though von Platen did not himself produce the first synthetic diamonds, he did create a machine with unique capabilities.

Today the Quintus press is used in powder metallurgy for the manufacturing of complex products, which are difficult to make due to their basic materials or their form. In the so-called HIP method (Hot Isostatic Pressure), production occurs in two steps: first, powdered metal is produced by finely breaking up a stream of molten metal, and then the powder is pressed into a dense form.

PRESSDUCTOR® TRANSDUCER

The Pressductor® transducer, a tool for measuring mechanical forces, was invented by Birgit Dahle and Orvar Dahle in 1953. The Pressductor consists of a sheet of magnetic material with two windings of wire at right angles to one another, so that their interior inductance is zero. When the device is put under torque the conductivity of the magnetic material is modified and the mutual inductance of the wire windings is also changed, so that a signal from one winding is transferred to the other. The strength of the signal depends upon the strength of the force.

The Pressductor is used to measure pressure in rolling mills, scales, etc. Another application is in the portable truck scales often used by highway police, e.g. to weigh an entire truck with a full load. Because the Pressductor is extremely durable, it can be integrated into large projects for continuous monitoring of loads upon machinery, such as derricks and overhead cranes.

FLYMO

The hovering lawn mower "Flymo" attracted considerable attention when it was introduced in 1953. Developed by Sven Kamph, it proved to be a simple but ingenious device.

This lawn mower is based upon the same principle as the hovercraft. A fan forces air downward under the body of the hovercraft, which is lifted slightly so that it floats on a cushion of air. Kamph used this principle to get his lawn mower to hover a few centimeters over the ground. The rotary blade used to cut the grass also served as the fan, so that the machine could be made small and compact. The mower is easy to use since the air cushion makes it feel weightless. At the same time the outward flow of air distributes the grass clippings, eliminating the need to rake them up. Kamph's mower is also easy to use on slopes and over drop-offs. The mower is sold under the name Flymo, and since its introduction more than 500,000 have been manufactured.

V-RING

Rotating axles always rest upon one or more bearings, which must be lubricated to maintain their proper function. The lubricating grease should stay in the bearing, preferably for a long time. This is why bearings have seals designed to keep grease in and water and dirt out. In their work to develop more effective seals, engineers Carl-Gustaf Derman and Sven-Erik Malmström of SKF produced an axle seal named the O-ring. While it was a good product, it was problematic due to its round cross-section. Derman and Malmström knew it would be much easier to mass produce rubber sealant rings if they could be cut with knife edges and experimented with a hexagonal cross-section. The waste materials from these experiments would later spawn a new invention.

Among the waste scraps were V-shaped pieces. Derman realized that they had found a very simple seal with many potential uses. The V-ring was discovered in 1959. However, their company was not interested, so the inventors started their own enterprise and built their own machine for production of the V-ring.

The invention was sold to Forsheda Rubber, a company which realized the potential of the new seal. Today the V-ring is part of the front wheels of all Volvo automobiles. Later, SKF became a large customer.

Today the V-ring is used in washing machines, cars, and rolling mills. Derman still works as an independent inventor. Among his many inventions is a shock absorber for boats.

THORSMAN PLUG

The Thorsman plug was invented by sociologist Oswald Thorsman. It is used to fasten screws into holes which cannot be threaded. Thorsman experimented with various plugs in his kitchen in Bromma, a suburb of Stockholm. He hoped to construct a durable plug for use in the high-rise apartments which were to be built between 1956 and 1962 at Hötorget in central Stockholm. Aluminum plugs eventually turned to powder, and wooden plugs dried out or rotted. The Thorsman plug was made of plastic, a revolutionary idea for the day. Furthermore, since it expanded outwards in two directions when tightened, it produced a double effect, giving it great resistance to being pulled out. Thorsman & Co. was founded in 1959.

THYRISTOR-CONTROLLED LOCOMOTIVE

Often when a train began moving, the power of the locomotive was too great and its wheels began to spin. Unfortunately, the weight of the loads which a locomotive had to pull could vary greatly. In 1960 a Swedish group under the leadership of Tore Nordin found a solution. Through the use of thyristors, a spin-free application of the locomotive's power was achieved regardless of the weight of the train's load.

High-tension alternating current was transformed into pulsating direct current, which was then fed to the four electric drive motors. The drive motors are mounted in two bogeys, where they each drive their own wheel. They are regulated by "drive controls" which control the thyristors so that the appropriate current is fed to the motors. The thyristor is a device which controls the "appearance" of the electric pulse without moving parts. In turn it also controls the electrical effect delivered to the electric motors of the locomotive. Thyristor-controlled "Rc-locomotives" can be used with various current strengths and frequencies. These locomotives have been a major Swedish export product manufactured by ABB. Today they are produced by a foreign manufacturer.

STRAIGHT LINE FLOW SHIPBUILDING

Nils Svensson revolutionized shipbuilding. Starting with a model built in his cellar, he created an entirely new way to build large ocean craft. His method laid the groundwork for the revolutionary Arendal Shipyard in Gothenburg.

Construction of the Arendal Shipyard was begun in 1959. In contrast to conventional shipyards, the Arendal facility was built with a relatively short face toward the water and a long section on dry land. This formation made it possible to create a "straight line flow" production line, beginning with the assembly of framework members and steel plating almost a kilometer from the water.

From there, the materials were transported along rollerways in a sequential order from station to station in various workshops until they reached the hull assembly building. Here, under a roof in the innermost portion of the shipyard, the panels, plate and framing members were welded together into slice-like sections. The aft section of the ship was built first.

In Svensson's system, section is joined to section, and the finished portions of the ship are "extruded" out into the outer portion of the yard. When the final section is welded into place, the ship is finished. What remains to be done before the ship can be delivered is merely finishing work such as painting and testing.

When the Arendal Shipyard was officially opened in 1963 the only thing it had in common with traditional shipyards was that it was a place for building ships.

Eventually, technological developments surpassed the Arendal Shipyard. During the global shipbuilding crisis of the mid-1970's, the Arendal facility concentrated on the offshore market, and achieved success with another innovation—half-submerged, floating platforms. In 1989 the shipyard's owner (the Swedish state) decided to end all shipbuilding activity at Arendal.

FLOFREEZE

Although deep freezing is an effective method for the preservation of food, it is difficult to freeze many fresh foods such as vegetables, berries, fruit and potatoes. Deep freezing had been used early on, but when the food was thawed, the results were often disappointing.

In 1961 Per Oscar Persson and Göran Lundahl developed a process in which vegetables were flash-frozen in liquid nitrogen, dubbed "Flofreeze." Persson and Lundahl found that freezing portions of food almost instantly gave the best results.

The liquid freezing medium means that the vegetables can be spread out and separated from one another during freezing. Since the introduction of this method, frozen foods have replaced many types of canned foods. Facilities for fluidized freezing using Persson's and Lundahl's method have since been built in most markets.

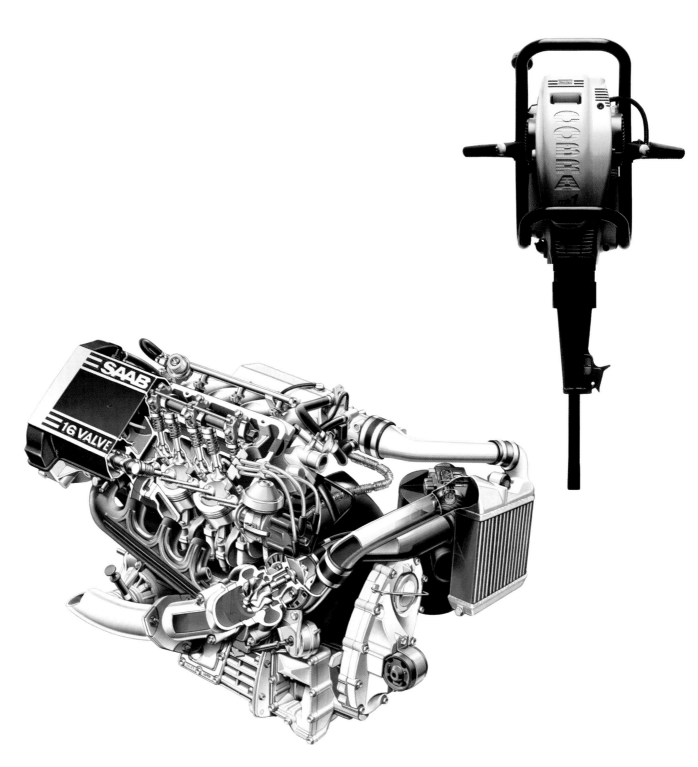

LEFT: SAAB TURBO ENGINE WITH 16 VALVES. RIGHT: THE ATLAS COPCO "COBRA" ROCK DRILL, DESIGNED BY BJÖRN DAHLSTRÖM.

HYDRAULIC ROCK DRILL

Hydraulic rock drill is a star product for Sweden's export industries, in particular for Atlas Copco. The first hydraulic rock drill was sold in 1973. These drills offer greater power and depth capacity than pneumatic rock drills. In addition, they are lighter and easier to move than earlier drill equipment, use less energy and contribute to improved working conditions.

One of the most important components of these drills is a recoil damping system invented in 1975 by Viggo Romell, chief engineer and project manager, engineer Åke Eklöf and Anders Fensborn. Atlas Copco has also developed handheld pneumatic and gasoline-driven rock drills (the "Cobra") which operate at low vibration levels. They significantly decrease the occurrence of "white fingers," a problem which afflicts many people who work for long periods of time with vibrating machines. Atlas Copco has been awarded prizes for the design of its handheld rock drills.

SAAB TURBO ENGINE

Although supercharged (or "turbo") engines had been used for many years in motor racing, they were not available to everyday drivers because they were difficult to maintain, unreliable and had poor fuel economy. Before turbo engines could be used in mass-produced passenger cars, these problems had to be overcome.

In 1976, as a project manager at Saab-Scania, Bengt Gadefelt developed a turbo engine for passenger cars. He applied a new idea to turbo technology, namely that the turbocharger took effect automatically when the driver needed extra power, for example when passing other cars or at highway speeds. Saab built the first mass-produced passenger car with a supercharged engine for everyday use. The new engine earned Saab more international press coverage than all of the company's previous PR efforts put together.

These developments continued and in 1984 Saab became one of the first car manufacturers in the world to market a mass-produced car equipped with a four-cylinder engine with 16 valves and turbo charging.

Saab has had many imitators and today most car manufacturers produce cars with turbo engines.

AXE SYSTEM

The AXE system is a completely automated telephone system that uses computerized switchboards developed by Swedish Telecom (now called Telia) in cooperation with Ericsson, with production taking place at Ericsson.

In 1969 Ericsson and Swedish Telecom were experiencing serious problems with their new computerized telephone switchboard stations. The dire situation gave rise to a collaborative development project undertaken in a jointly-owned research company, Ellemtel. Ellemtel was started in 1970 with stock holdings of SEK 10 million. In addition, both Swedish Telecom and Ericsson invested SEK 20 million each in the form of loans to the company, which can in retrospect be regarded as a wise investment.

Bengt Gunnar Magnusson (1925–1995), the originator of the idea, also served as project manager. The first AXE facility began service in the town of Södertälje, south of Stockholm.

With the AXE system Ericsson underwent a huge expansion. AXE offered customers access to a variety of services such as wake-up calls, forwarding of incoming calls to other telephones, fast dialing of frequently-used numbers, and more. AXE became the basis for the telephone systems of today.

No matter where in the world people pick up a telephone handset, the AXE system is involved. AXE will continue to be one of the main components in the global infrastructure of traditional landline and mobile communications for both speech and data. One of the first nations to make full use of the system was Australia. AXE is the most widely-used switchboard system, with more than 250 million users in over 135 countries, on 150 million land-based and over 100 million mobile telephone lines.

During the final years of the 20th century, AXE was the most-frequently installed system for land-based telephone lines, and sales of AXE for use in mobile telephone systems are three times higher than for land-based networks. AXE systems that were installed in the 1980s are still in use around the world, and they are fully compatible with today's telephone technology.

MOBILE (CELLULAR) TELEPHONY

The basis for mobile (cellular) telephony was established in the 1950s. The equipment was clumsy and the range was short. Nonetheless, the system showed promise. In 1968 Östen Mäkitalo became head of a research group at Ericsson. The dream that everyone could own a mobile telephone existed even at that early stage even if the technological means did not.

As electronic components shrank in size and microchips were developed, an intense worldwide race began to create a first-generation wireless telephone system. In 1976 Mäkitalo's group drew up their guidelines for Network Management Technologies (NMT), a wireless telephone system for everyone. The idea was based not on existing technology, but on technology that was expected to come several years later.

The tactic was a success. In the beginning of the 1980s NMT made its breakthrough in modern mobile telephony. When NMT was introduced, the media made the claim that "Portable telephones have finally become portable." Sweden had taken on a leading role in mobile telephone technology. At the same time, work began on today's Global System for Mobile Communication, or GSM.

Ericsson took advantage of their head start and during the 1990s became the world's leading seller of mobile telephone systems. In this extremely high-growth industry, Ericsson has since had to relinquish its leadership role in mobile telephones to other manufacturers who are more specialized in consumer sales.

In 1885 Stockholm had more telephones per capita than any other city in the world. A little more than 100 years later, Sweden had more mobile telephones per capita than almost any other country thanks to Ericsson. Östen Mäkitalo remained at Ericsson and has led the development of a number of projects, including GSM, RDS (a computer system for mobile radio), MBS (beepers) and Dualband, which allows mobile telephones to switch between different bandwidths.

HÅKAN LANS.

COMPUTER MOUSE, COLOR SCREEN GRAPHICS FOR COMPUTERS, AND GP&C

Håkan Lans is one of Sweden's most famous living inventors. He began inventing as a boy, finding inspiration in the odd items in the cellar of his father's pawn shop. At the age of twelve, he built a go-cart powered by a moped motor. A few years later he constructed a miniature submarine which could dive to a depth of more than 100 meters. Today he is best known for three major inventions: the computer mouse, color computer graphics and GP&C (Global Positioning & Communication).

Lans constructed a digitizer, also known as a "pointer," consisting of a small box that had one button, attached to a light table by an electrical cord. The device was manufactured and sold in great numbers by Houston Instruments. Because other inventors introduced similar methods of controlling computers at around the same time, Lans' copyright on the computer mouse has been disputed.

Although color TV did exist when Lans first introduced his color graphics for computers, most felt that black and white screens were completely sufficient for all computer needs. Today his color graphics are used by almost all computer manufacturers.

Lans called his third great invention "GP&C," an extension of the GPS Global Positioning System satellite navigation developed by the American military. With GPS, pilots, navigators and automobile drivers can see exactly where they are. With Håkan Lans' GP&C system they can also see where other aircraft, ships and cars are.

In 1999, Lans' system was accepted as the international standard for ocean traffic, and in 2000 also as the international standard for air traffic. If this system had existed earlier, many terrible air collisions might have been avoided. Using this system, aircraft can fly closer to one another's routes, reducing overall flying time. In the future GP&C may be put to use in highway traffic to direct vehicles centrally, which could bring great improvements to the transport sector.

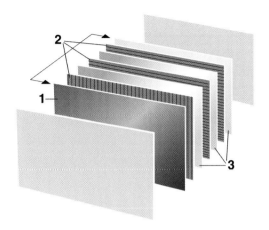

WELDING HELMET WITH LIQUID CRYSTAL VISOR

Åke Hörnell is the man behind an innovation which has improved working conditions for welders around the world—a welding helmet with a visor that automatically darkens when the light from the welding arc strikes the helmet's sensors. The visor lightens again automatically as soon as the arc is broken and the welder can move on to the next task without having to raise or lower the visor. In combination with the new ergonomic shape of the helmet this visor has greatly simplified the work of modern welders.

Hörnell's visor and helmet are based upon an invention he developed in 1972 for his final year project at the Chalmers University of Technology in Gothenburg. At the Götaverken Shipyards Hörnell was employed to find better glass for welders' visors. In this role, a Swiss discovery from 1974—"liquid crystals," which reacted immediately to light—caught his attention. After several years at Götaverken he once again delved into research on the new technology of liquid crystals. He had an idea to create eyeglasses for light-sensitive persons using liquid crystals. Given Hörnell's knowledge of welding, it was no great leap for him to apply this technology to welding visors. By 1978 he had created a prototype. The Swedish welding supplies company ESAB declined, and as Hörnell was unable to interest anyone in his invention he started his own company.

Today Hörnell's idea for an automatic welding visor provides work for nearly 100 people in Sweden, as well as other employees abroad. Approximately 120,000 helmets are sold yearly, with sales in almost all industrialized nations. The company continues to develop new products, such as the "Speedglas 9000." Developed in collaboration with Ergonomi Design Gruppen, this helmet received the 1997 European Design Prize. The company has also developed a battery-driven air filter, which removes 98% of the toxic substances in welding fumes.

LEFT: DEVELOPED IN COLLABORATION WITH ERGONOMI DESIGN GRUPPEN, THIS WELDING HELMET RECEIVED THE 1997 EUROPEAN DESIGN PRIZE. TOP: THE VISOR IS MADE OF A LAMINATE OF SEVEN DIFFERENT LAYERS: (1) A UV/IR FILTER, (2) THREE LIGHT-POLARIZING LAYERS, (3) THREE LAYERS OF LIQUID CRYSTAL, AND AN OUTER LAYER OF GLASS.

FUNCTIONAL WORK CLOTHES

Electrician Matti Viio was annoyed over poorly-designed work clothes. He thought that the clothes just got in his way. The straps of his overalls kept pulling loose, and when he tied the straps together so that he would not lose his overalls, the knots dug into his shoulders. He found his pockets poorly suited to carrying staples and nails.

Matti Viio tried to get clothing factories to make work clothes that were better adapted to work, but the companies answered that this would be too expensive and difficult. Viio took the matter into his own hands.

In 1975, after some years of experimentation, he started Snickers Original on the concept of "practical work clothes for all situations." His endeavors succeeded beyond all expectations and the company grew rapidly. Over the years, Snickers has gained many competitors, and today almost every field of work has its own special work clothes adapted to its specific needs.

CASH ADAPTER

At the age of 17, after just eight years of compulsory school and a short time as an apprentice in a radio shop, Leif Lundblad started his first company, a TV repair shop. An excavator caught his interest and this led to a new entrepreneurial experiment with that type of machine. Then came a new company that used hydraulic "skylift" platforms for cleaning building facades. After that, Lundblad invented his highly successful cash payment device for gasoline pumps, which made it possible to pay at the pump with bank notes.

In 1976 came the idea for what was to become Leif Lundblad's greatest success yet, a cash machine that could handle bank notes. A major drawback with the first automated teller machines was their inefficiency in handling notes. Bank personnel had to cull out the worn notes and then manually push the usable ones in between a set of metal bands. Around 1978 Lundblad solved this problem by placing the notes in a magazine. This made it possible to use all of the notes, and they could even be of different denominations. This greatly reduced the work involved with these machines.

Lundblad's invention found applications not only in automated teller machines, but in banks themselves, wherever large quantities of notes had to be handled.

In 1976 Lundblad started his Inter Innovation company to manufacture his note handler and other inventions. Ten years after it was started, the company had 2,000 employees and sales of SEK 1.2 billion. In 1996 the company was sold to a foreign investor.

THREE-POINT SAFETY BELT

For years Nils Bohlin worked as a technician in Saab's aircraft division. He helped develop the ejection seat for the famous J35 Draken fighter aircraft. In 1958 he switched from aircraft to automobiles and began a new job at Volvo.

At that time, seat belts were already standard equipment in some car models, but they were only two-point belts, which went across the hips or diagonally across the torso. With such seat belts there was still a sizeable risk of slipping out of the belt in a collision and being thrown from the car.

Bohlin became Volvo's first safety engineer, and was assigned the task of finding a better design. His solution was the three-point safety belt: one strap across the torso and one across the hips, with a fixed hitching point between the seats. This belt stayed in the correct place during a collision. The powerful forces of a collision were distributed to the pelvis, one of the most durable parts of the body, and the ribcage, which is fairly flexible. Thus the soft organs of the abdomen could be protected. All tests showed that the belt worked well, and in 1959 the three-point belt was introduced as standard equipment in the front seats of Volvo's passenger cars for the Nordic market. However, Volvo had set its sights on the USA.

In 1968 the large American car manufacturers accepted the three-point safety belt as standard equipment in the front seats of all passenger cars. Since then, the three-point belt has spread around the world and has saved tens of thousands of lives. The three-point belt has spared many people from injuries which might have left them disabled for life. Nils Bohlin and Volvo have received a number of honors for their development of the three-point safety belt and their documentation of its advantages.

In 1989 Nils Bohlin was inducted into the Safety Hall of Fame. When the West German patent authority celebrated its one hundredth anniversary some years earlier, it honored eight patents which had been of the greatest importance for humanity. The three-point safety belt was one of these, and Bohlin was ranked equal in importance to other names from automobile history such as Edison, Benz and Diesel.

Figures maintained by the National Highway Traffic Safety Administration in the USA reveal just how important the safety belt has been for humanity. They show that, in the 1980s, eleven lives were saved by safety belts each day. This amounts to a life saved every other hour or 4,000 lives per year in the USA alone.

Today, all three-point safety belts use the design developed by Nils Bohlin, regardless of the make of the car. The safety belt is one of the most important car safety features.

RETRACTABLE SEAT BELT

Cars had been equipped with safety belts for many years, but earlier belts hung loose and were difficult to adjust. Different drivers using the same car were forced to readjust the length of the belt. If one needed to reach for something, for example in the glove compartment, the belt had to be released. The type of safety belt dominant today—the retractable belt—eliminates these drawbacks.

Attempts to produce a functional retractable seatbelt met with several difficulties—the spring that was to retract the belt was too weak and became weaker with time, and the locking mechanism did not function satisfactorily and was affected by dirt. In the early 1960s Hans Karlsson, a helicopter mechanic at Ostermans, began work on an improved belt. His efforts led to the introduction of the retractable seat belt in 1961. This invention was improved by its inventor several times until 1972.

The retractable belt was a great improvement on earlier fixed seat belts. It is always pulled close to the body without squeezing. It is self-adjusting, fits all body types, rolls out of the way when it is released and is easy to put on and take off. However, the most important feature is the action of the locking roller. It has a double locking function: it has a "shock lock" when pulled out rapidly and a retarded locking action when the speed of the car is reduced more gradually.

Hans Karlsson has also produced other inventions, such as a balancing pulley for the suspension of handheld tools. This pulley is based upon the principle of "reversed spring power" which provides constant tension on a line, even when pulled a considerable distance. Karlsson is still active as an inventor and is working on a vibration-free, fuel-efficient two-stroke motor. He has already been granted a patent in Sweden and has applied for patents in several other countries.

AIRBAG SENSOR

Airbags for front-end crashes have been in existence since the 1970s. Airbags for side collisions are a relatively new development. A problem with side crash bags was that they had to be inflated much faster than front crash bags, but existing technology would not allow this.

The solution to this problem was found by engineers Staffan Carlsson and Torsten Persson in the town of Karlskoga. With the help of modern pyrotechnology they developed a sensor which reacted quickly enough. The sensor sends a signal to the gas generator which inflates the airbag. The entire process occurs in a fraction of a second.

The sensor was put into production in 1994 and has since come into use around the world. It is used in for example Saab and Volvo cars. Sales are around 700,000 sensors per year, and about 50 people are employed fulltime in its manufacture.

Side crashes account for about one quarter of all collisions, but because the sides of a car are thin and the distance to the passengers is shorter, these accidents are responsible for one third of all serious car injuries. Around half of all side collisions lead to head injuries. In the USA alone, side collisions cause 2,400 deaths and 60,000 serious injuries per year. Side airbags providing head protection could save the lives of around 600 people per year and greatly reduce injuries in the USA alone.

REAR-FACING CHILD SAFETY SEAT

Professor Bertil Aldman (1925–1998) has made many pioneering contributions to traffic safety and biomechanics. He is internationally known, especially for his development of the world's first rear-facing child safety seat.

The year was 1957 and Sweden's national research councils had organized a joint committee on traffic safety research. Traffic accidents were on the rise during this period and the committee was looking for a physician willing to devote himself to this type of research. Aldman registered his interest and was given the task of examining the problem.

Studies were made on safety belts, traffic accidents and the treatment of the injured. Tests were made of all types of safety systems for both adults and children that could be found on the market. Very little was known about how much bodily stress children could withstand during an accident. The studies showed that existing safety systems were insufficient, especially those that had been developed for children, as most of them could not withstand the forces they were supposed to.

At a symposium in the USA, Aldman saw a proposal for how astronauts would be placed during takeoff and landing, when the forces of acceleration or deceleration can be almost as high as in a traffic accident. The astronauts would lie on their backs and absorb the force with their entire body and head simultaneously. The head and body were not to move in relation to one another during acceleration.

Aldman thought this solution would also be good for children in cars, and in 1963 he developed a prototype which his youngest son got to test during trips around the Stockholm area. The child seat was soon put into production, and in 1988 Sweden passed its law regarding compulsory child safety seats for children in cars. As a result, injuries to children in car accidents have been dramatically reduced. In Sweden it is felt that other types of child seats are not suitable for children up to three years of age. Small children have weak necks in relation to the weight of their heads, making support for their heads during a collision very important.

Bertil Aldman also collaborated on work to develop a seat belt cushion for somewhat larger children. Similar solutions were presented simultaneously in different parts of the world.

HALDEX ALL-WHEEL DRIVE

An invention created in a workshop in the western Swedish town of Trollhättan may be one of the greatest innovations in the area of four-wheel drive in the last few years. The Haldex AWD coupling has begun to catch on around the world. Volkswagen held the production rights until autumn 1999, but since then other car manufacturers have begun to use the system and others are waiting in line as the interest in all-wheel drive (AWD) continues to grow.

Four-wheel drive (4WD) is nothing new—heavy-terrain vehicles have been equipped with it for years. About 60% of today's four-wheel drive systems use simple, manual "on-off" systems for switching between two-wheel and four-wheel drive, whereas other vehicles are equipped with a full-time four-wheel drive system in which all four wheels drive the vehicle at all times.

In the late 1980s a mechanically-minded car racer, Sigvard Johansson from Trollhättan, found that none of the 4WD systems he had tried worked satisfactorily. He began to build his own system. Johansson succeeded, but the development work became too involved and he turned over the production to the technical firm Haldex, which has developed the product since 1992.

In later years four-wheel drive has been used for more than just getting around in heavy terrain. It provides greatly improved driving characteristics and safety in situations such as hydroplaning on wet roads.

Haldex has developed a coupling that can work in conjunction with other safety systems requiring quick mechanical action, such as ABS, TCS and ESP.

The Haldex AWD coupling is a compact mechanical, hydraulic unit with integrated electronics. It is linked to other systems in the car, so no additional sensors are needed. The coupling delivers different effects adapted to road conditions without direct input from the driver. The unit can be described as a hydraulic pump equipped with a disc clutch located between incoming and outgoing shafts. The pump is activated by differences in the speeds at which the wheels rotate, for example when the wheels spin on slick surfaces. The pump is not active during normal driving. When there is a difference in the wheel speeds the clutch discs are pressed together and the wheel spinning ceases. The system reacts in one tenth of a second.

As Haldex AWD has gained international recognition, more foreign car manufacturers are placing orders. Volvo has decided to use the Haldex system in its S 60 AWD and XC 90 models.

POWERFORMER AND MOTORFORMER

Mats Leijon, currently a professor at Uppsala University, has registered more patents through ABB than any other inventor in recent years. One major innovation he has led the development of is the "Powerformer." It replaces the transformer and makes a middle stage between high-tension lines and the generator unnecessary. In the long term it will lead to energy savings.

A series of products has been developed using the technology of the Powerformer, among them the "Motorformer," a new electric motor.

What distinguishes this new series of generators and motors from conventional technology is that the rotor is wound with fully insulated wire. This construction makes it possible to operate the motor using high-tension electricity with a higher output than conventional motors.

Total energy losses are reduced, since this motor does not need a transformer or the control equipment that electric motors normally require. Among other things, there is no need for a breaker between the motor and the transformer to protect the motor in case of a power surge.

When Mats Leijon began working at ABB Corporate Research in Västerås, he was determined to build a high-tension electrical generator. Although conventional wisdom held that this was impossible, Leijon found no fundamental limitations in Maxwell's Laws. After three years of consideration and calculation, he was ready to present his idea to the corporate management. Leijon was given the freedom to develop his idea, and the project was guarded in high secrecy. During the five years it took to develop the Powerformer generator, not one word leaked out.

The development of the Powerformer itself is no less than remarkable. As soon as the blueprints were ready, a functional Powerformer facility was built in just 18 months at the Porjus power station in northern Sweden. The station was formally opened in June 1998.

Powerformer technology, with its rounded, polymer insulated high-tension cables in the rotor windings, is legally protected by more than 200 patents. Other components in the system are for the most part the same as in ABB's conventional products.

The Motorformer is the world's first electric motor that can operate on unadulterated high-tension alternating current. These motors can reduce a factory's energy losses by about 25%. They can be used in all types of industry, but are especially useful in the processing of raw materials, for example to operate large pumps or machines. The Motorformer motor uses the same technology as the Powerformer high-tension generator.

During recent years the number of inventions presented by ABB has increased dramatically to more than 600 per year.

SELF-OPERATING VACUUM CLEANER

A self-operating vacuum cleaner which navigates by ultrasound, like a bat, is the world's first automatic household vacuum cleaner in mass production. It has three settings: normal, fast, and localized cleanup. It finds its charging station automatically. If cleaning is not finished when the vacuum cleaner needs charging it will continue cleaning where it left off after two hours of recharging. After cleaning it puts itself in "sleep" mode.

Electrolux introduced this vacuum cleaner as a prototype in 1997 and today it is sold on the market. Per Ljunggren led a development team which consisted of about 50 people. Prehistoric animals inspired the shape of the vacuum cleaner, which was named the "Trilobite." It received a great deal of attention for its unusual design and was included in an exhibition at the National Museum of Fine Arts in Stockholm. The Trilobite was designated the most exciting design product of 1997 in the book "100 Designs, 100 Years: Innovative Designs of the 20th Century" (1999). The Trilobite's exterior form was designed by Inese Ljunggren.

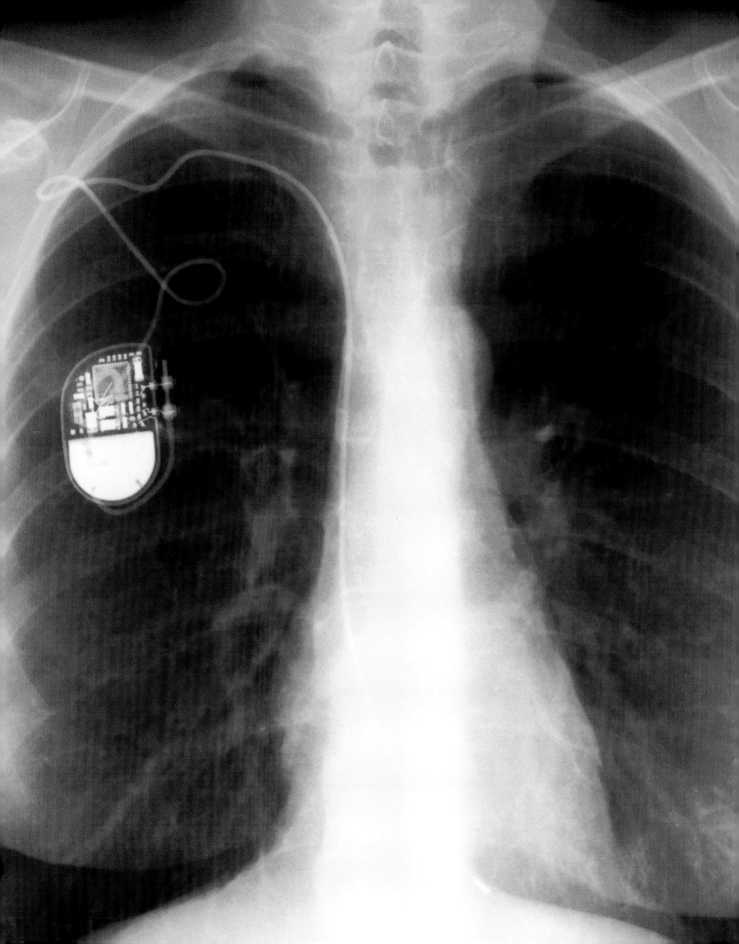

SWEDISH MEDICAL INNOVATIONS

PACEMAKER

Physician Rune Elmqvist developed a small, battery-operated pacemaker to stimulate contractions of the heart muscle when the heart's natural impulses are too weak.

As early as the beginning of the 1800s, physicians had dreamt of increasing the frequency of the heartbeat through electrical impulses. In the 1950s this idea was realized, and in 1958 Rune Elmqvist built his first pacemaker, a device so small that it could be surgically implanted. That same year, Professor Åke Senning (1915–2000) performed the world's first pacemaker operation at the Karolinska Hospital in Stockholm. The two researchers had cooperated for many years. In 1948 Elmqvist had built a defibrillator for Senning that could stop the pumping of the heart and then start it again.

According to the story, the first pacemaker was molded in the bottom of a coffee cup. It was 55 mm in diameter and 16 mm thick and had a frequency of 72 beats per minute, with a pulse length of 2 milliseconds. Elmqvist was able to construct the device because he had obtained some of the first silicon transistors ever imported into Sweden. It took him 14 days to build his pacemaker.

A modern pacemaker weighs 14 to 40 g and can be implanted with local anesthesia. Electrodes connect the pacemaker to the heart via the veins. The speed of modern pacemakers can be adjusted according to the needs of the individual patient. Adjustments are made by telemetry, using radio contact between the pacemaker and the doctor's programming unit. This also makes it possible to obtain diagnostic information. Efforts are underway to create pacemakers which automatically sense the patient's needs.

Current pacemakers have a battery life of up to ten years, after which they are replaced, and there are now rechargeable types as well. This device has helped many patients live a normal life. Today more than one million people have implanted pacemakers.

In 1948 Rune Elmqvist also invented the Minograph, an ink jet printer that could register rapid changes. The Minograph was used in ECG machines, and a modernized version is still in use today.

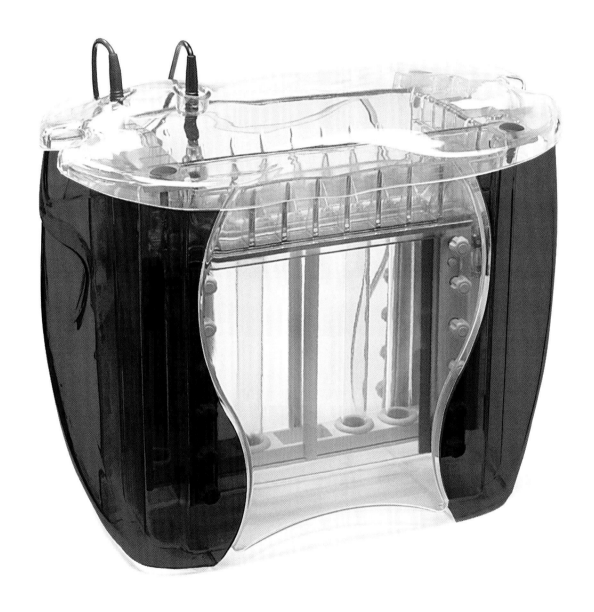

HOEFER™ SE 600 RUBY FROM AMERSHAM BIOSCIENCES HAS BEEN THE WORLDWIDE LABORATORY STANDARD SYSTEM FOR GEL ELECTROPHORESIS SEPARATIONS FOR YEARS. COPYRIGHT AMERSHAM BIOSCIENCES 2002. (COURTESY OF AMERSHAM BIOSCIENCES.)

ELECTROPHORESIS

Electrophoresis is a method for the analysis of different proteins based upon the fact that molecules can be negatively, positively or neutrally charged in different environments. The method was developed by chemist Arne Tiselius (1902–1971) during the 1930s and 1940s. He constructed devices that used capillary zone electrophoresis to show that blood plasma from a human being could be divided into several fractures.

In electrophoresis, molecules mixed into a gel such as Sephadex, are exposed to an electrical field causing them to move in different directions and at different rates. Positively charged particles move toward the minus pole and negatively charged particles move toward the plus pole. If the electrical field is constant, the speed of the particles will be determined by the charge they hold, their size and shape, as well as by the strength of the field and the viscosity of the liquid. This is why electrophoresis plays such an important role in the separation of molecules and particles in complex mixtures. Electrophoresis is an effective tool for the determination of the genetic material contained in DNA.

Electrophoresis is used for both analysis and separation. The most commonly used medium is water that has been made electrically conductive through the addition of electrolytes. The electrolyte systems are often buffered, that is, they have the capacity to hold pH levels at a desired constant.

In other methods of electrophoresis, the solution is surrounded by a porous matrix, usually a gel medium which slows the flow within the liquid and keeps the separated components from reuniting. The interaction between characteristics of the matrix, for example pore size, and the surrounded reagents is often used to advantage.

Tiselius' work has been continued by other researchers who have developed many different methods for analysis and separation based on the principles of electrophoresis. The pioneering work done by Tiselius has taken on great importance in modern medical and biological research. Along with the ultracentrifuge it is an important part of modern laboratory equipment. Arne Tiselius received the Nobel Prize in Chemistry in 1948.

SEPHADEX

Sephadex is a medium discovered in 1958 by researchers Björn Ingelman, Per Flodin and Jerker Porath. Sephadex consists of molecules of dextran, a polysaccharide which had been known for many years. These molecules can be made to cross-bind, resulting in a three-dimensional network. This discovery led to further developments in the separation technology of electrophoresis (see above).

The wound dressing Debrisan®, introduced in 1973, is another area of application for Sephadex. This salve utilizes the cleansing and absorbent properties of Sephadex.

Debrisan consists of a network of dextran chains in the form of small "pearls" which can absorb the moisture from a wound. This innovation came about after Assistant Professor Ulf Rothman accidentally dropped a can of dextran in water.

MACRODEX

Dextran is also used as a blood plasma substitute. For years, medical researchers around the world had been searching for an artificial plasma.

Researchers Björn Ingelman and Anders Grönwall discovered that dextran could be used as a blood substitute. Ingelman and Grönwall worked for Professor Arne Tiselius at Uppsala University's Department of Biochemistry. In 1943 Ingelman studied high level molecular substances found in sugar beets. A certain type of bacteria in sugar beet juices created an unusual high level molecular substance, which proved to be dextran. Ingelman injected this substance into rabbits in an attempt to produce an antiserum. He discovered that dextran had no antigenic properties, and his experiment failed. However, when the negative results revealed this peculiar lack of antigenic properties, Ingelman and Grönwall got the idea to use dextran as a blood replacement.

After initial experiments, a collaborative effort was established with the pharmaceuticals corporation Pharmacia for large-scale production of dextran. After comprehensive development work, the plasma substitute Macrodex was introduced in 1947. In 1961 a newer variant called Rheomacrodex was released. Macrodex increases the body's plasma volume and also helps prevent blood clots. Rheomacrodex has the additional benefit of improving circulation.

INTRALIPID®

In the 1940s nutritionist Arvid Wretlind had an idea for achieving a completely intravenous nutrient input as an alternative to normal food, for patients who could not eat. At the time, the idea was thought bizarre and the task impossible. Wretlind's first goal was to develop a preparation of amino acids to replenish the body's protein supply. This preparation was ready in 1944 and was dubbed Aminosol.

One problem remained: How was the patient to get a sufficient intake of energy without eating? Others had tried to solve this problem without success. Wretlind developed an emulsion of fats that could be introduced into the body via a drip.

His work resulted in the preparation Intralipid®, introduced by Vitrum in 1962. Many people around the world have had their nutritional requirements fulfilled thanks to this preparation, particularly in connection with unconsciousness, major operations, and severe burns. There are also reports of people who enjoy good physical health and can manage their jobs, even though they have been receiving all of their nourishment intravenously for several years.

BECAUSE XYLOCAINE® ANESTHETIZES ALMOST IMMEDIATELY, VISITS TO THE DENTIST ARE MUCH SHORTER THAN IN THE PAST.

XYLOCAINE®

Comprehensive experiments conducted by physicians Nils Löfgren (1913–1967) and Bengt Lundqvist (1906–1952) during the 1930s led to the introduction of the local anesthetic LL-30 in 1943. That same year, pharmaceutical company Astra took over the development of the drug, and in 1948 Xylocain® (in English, Xylocaine) was introduced. It brought about something of a revolution in local anesthesia, because it anesthetizes with virtually no delay. Xylocaine is still used around the world in odontology and other medical fields. Every day, over one million injections of this drug are given.

Xylocaine is also used to treat certain irregularities of the heartbeat, including heart attacks (as Xylocard®) and in the form of an ointment used for problems such as hemorrhoids (as Xyloproct®). Xylocaine is often used in conjunction with adrenaline, which contracts the blood vessels. This lengthens the effective period of the Xylocaine due to slower blood transport, and also reduces the risk of side effects since less of the drug reaches the bloodstream.

Nils Löfgren was also involved in the development of the local anesthetic Citanest® in 1957. This agent is similar to Xylocaine with fewer side effects.

83

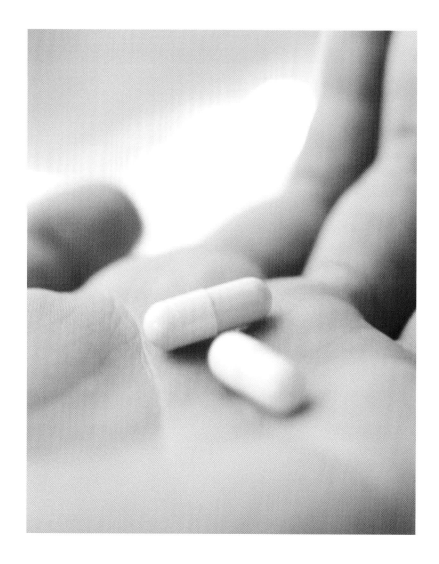

TIME-RELEASE TABLETS

In 1955 researchers Lars-Einar Fryklöf (1929–1999), Erik Sandell and Ivan Östholm developed a method of time-delayed medication they named "durettes." These tablets work on the principle that their active ingredient is released after they are ingested. Time-release tablets are made of coated grains of medicine imbedded in a material which breaks down slowly in the digestive tract. Another method involves surrounding the tablets with a polymer membrane that controls the diffusion of the medication into the liquids of the digestive tract. Since they contain larger amounts of medication than regular pills, time-release tablets must be swallowed whole, otherwise they may have too strong an effect. Time-release tablets have the advantage that patients do not need to take their medication as often, and that the release of the active ingredient is more even.

BETA BLOCKERS

In the early years of the 1960s, the research and development departments at three Swedish pharmaceutical corporations began research into receptor mechanisms. The project led to beta blockers, a new type of medicine for various diseases. Cell activity in the body is controlled by different "signal" substances. These signal substances exert their influence via "stations" in the cell known as receptors. The development of substances that seek out the receptors (or that have an "affinity" for the receptors and stimulate the cell to increased activity) has given rise to medications that improve the function of a particular organ, for example the heart.

Some important medicines that have resulted from this research include Aptin® (1965), a medicine against angina pectoris, Bricanyl® (1966), an asthma medicine with no undesirable side effects on the heart, and Seloken® (1970), a selective beta blocker that reduces blood pressure.

APTIN® is used in the treatment of diseases of the heart and arteries, to protect against extreme stimulus of the heart. Such exaggerated stimulus can occur during extreme emotional stress or during heavy physical work. In such cases the levels of adrenaline and/or noradrenaline in the blood increase. Adrenaline, a hormone, and noradrenaline, a signal substance, stimulate the heart since their molecules bind with special receptor points known as beta receptors. The molecules of the beta blocker also bind to these receptors without stimulating activity. Since the receptors are blocked, the adrenaline or noradrenaline is unable to locate a receptor, and thus do not stimulate the heart.

Aptin was developed at Hässle Pharmaceuticals in Gothenburg by three professors: Arne Brändström, Hans Corrodi and Bengt Åblad.

BRICANYL® is one of the most successful Swedish medications. Bricanyl was developed in 1966 by researchers Kjell Wetterlin and Leif A. Svensson at the Draco Pharmaceuticals in Lund. In order for an asthmatic to be able to breathe easier the smallest capillaries of the lungs, the bronchi, must be widened. In the 1960s it was felt that it was impossible to affect the bronchi without also affecting heart activity. However, while studying medical literature, Henry Persson at Draco found mention of an agent which had greater effect upon the bronchi than on the heart. Thus began intensive research, which eventually led to Bricanyl. By 1969 the researchers had synthesized a suitable substance, developed a means of large-scale production, tested the medication for side effects and had performed comprehensive tests on humans and laboratory animals so that the medication was ready to be released.

SELOKEN® is a selective beta blocker used as a heart medication. It reduces blood pressure and blocks pain sensations in the heart. Its primary advantage is that it limits injuries resulting from a heart attack and prevents new heart attacks. This is achieved primarily through an increased oxygen flow to the heart. Seloken is one of the most important blood pressure reducers. A patient can use it year after year without major side effects. The inventors of Seloken are the researchers Arne Brändström, Arvid Carlsson, Stig Å.I. Carlsson, Hans Corrodi, Lars Ek and Bengt Åblad, and the medicine was developed at Hässle Pharmaceuticals in Gothenburg.

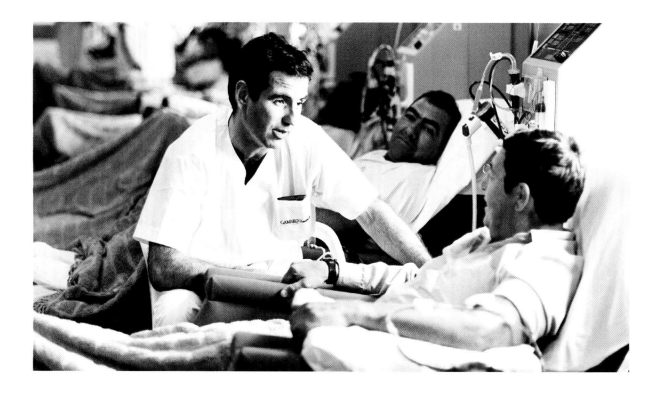

DIALYSIS MACHINE

The dialysis machine was invented in 1965 by Nils Alwall (1904–1986) and Lennart Östergren of Lund University. It was a device for one-time use, intended as a substitute for a kidney that had been injured or surgically removed. In dialysis, the patient is connected to a dialysis machine and the blood is filtered through the machine. Dialysis cleanses the blood of substances which in a healthy person would be passed in the urine once the kidneys had removed it.

As the human body breaks down nutrients, it also produces waste products which are carried away in the bloodstream. The blood is then cleaned by the kidneys. The kidneys also filter extra liquid out of the blood. In addition, the kidneys regulate the pH levels of the blood and are part of the system that produces red blood cells. The kidneys are vital organs that are normally impossible to live without. Through dialysis, it is possible to live a reasonably healthy life even when the kidneys have ceased to function.

Dialysis is also used in certain acute situations to cleanse the blood of poisons which might damage the kidneys (for example, when a patient has been poisoned or while awaiting transplantation of a new kidney). Dialysis prevents urine poisoning and increases the patient's prospects of a return to health.

Work on the first dialysis machine was begun in 1968. Since then the device has allowed hundreds of thousands of people to lead a reasonably normal life. Today 200,000 patients around the world are treated using this invention. A major manufacturer of dialysis machines is the Gambro Company, headquartered in Lund, southern Sweden, with branches in about ten countries. Gambro has sales in 103 countries and serves about 50,000 patients at 600 clinics worldwide.

DIGITAL HEARING AID

One of the most difficult problems for a person with impaired hearing is distinguishing human speech from disturbing background noise. The greatest disadvantage of most models of traditional analogue hearing aids is that they amplify all sound, including noises that the user would prefer not to hear. Researchers Johan Hellgren and Thomas Lunner have developed a solution to this problem. Under the leadership of Professor Stig Alinger at the University Hospital in Linköping they invented the technology behind Digifocus, the world's first digital hearing aid, which is marketed by a Danish company.

Digifocus is unique in that different portions of the "sound image" can be emphasized according to the unique hearing profile of the individual. Digifocus automatically adapts itself to different sound environments, making it easier to go from a noisy street to a quiet library without the inconvenience of having to manually adjust a hearing aid.

Digifocus was awarded the European Union's prestigious Technology Prize for 1996. Since its introduction in the spring of that same year, it has achieved widespread use. Today the device is recommended by hearing clinics around the world and is sold in about 40 countries, chiefly in Europe and USA.

TURBUHALER

Asthma is often related to inflammatory diseases of the respiratory passages. It is estimated that 5 to 10% of the adult population in industrialized countries suffer from asthma. Yet the exact cause of asthma remains unknown. Persons afflicted with asthma have become one of the largest target groups for the pharmaceuticals industry. AstraZeneca Pharmaceuticals in Lund has developed several major products for its treatment including Symbicort®, Pulmicort®, and Bricanyl®. However, it was difficult to determine the proper dosages of these medications and overdoses were common. Also, some of the medicine always remained in the empty packaging and was wasted. A better means of setting the dosages was needed.

Researcher Kjell Wetterlin at Draco in Lund has developed the Turbuhaler, an inhaler that provides a simpler and more effective way to take asthma medication than by earlier means. The development work on the Turbuhaler began in 1970 and took about ten years.

The Turbuhaler is pre-charged with a certain number of doses. Each dose is exactly the same quantity, reducing the risks of under- or overdosage. The user simply inhales deeply. Unlike earlier inhalers, no propellent gases are necessary since the medication is moved along by the patient's inhalation.

This new inhaler is more effective due to its precision, and because its construction allows more than double the distribution of the medication in the lungs than with earlier inhalers. In turn this allows the use of smaller doses to achieve the same effect. The Turbuhaler is made of an environment-friendly plastic which over time breaks down into carbon dioxide and water.

The development of this inhaler was a new area for AstraZeneca, since the company had previously developed only medicinal substances. With the Turbuhaler, AstraZeneca moved into the production of technical aids for dispensing medications. Today this new area is an important part of the research pursued by the company at its facilities in Lund.

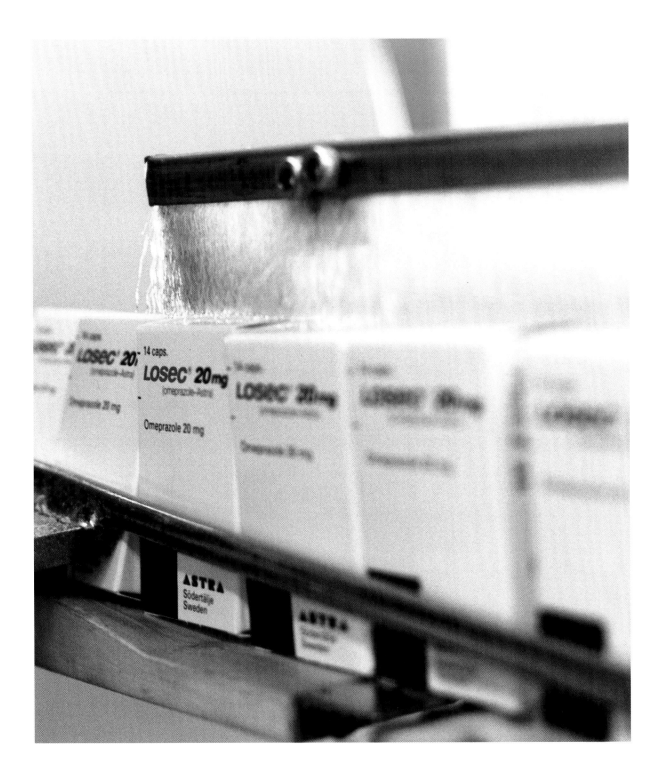

L O S E C ®

Losec® differs from all previous ulcer medications. It works on only one type of cell in the entire body: the type that produces gastric acid. As a result, the side effects of this product are minimal. The "secret" of Losec is its ability to prevent the formation of gastric acid in the stomach.

Hässle Pharmaceuticals' ulcer project began in 1964. The need for better ulcer medications was great since 10–15% of the population is afflicted by ulcers sooner or later. Since it was known that one of the main causes of ulcers was excessive production of gastric acid by certain cells in the lining of the stomach, the project sought a substance that could inhibit this acid production.

Sven Erik Sjöstrand joined the project in the summer of 1972 and in 1973 Ulf Ljunggren discovered a substance called H 123/26, which unfortunately proved to be poisonous. H 123/26 was modified, and in 1978 the Losec molecule was synthesized. Losec was made available for sale in Sweden in 1988. During the development years the project was nearly discontinued on several occasions, but managed to survive.

Numerous clinical studies have shown that Losec is more effective than earlier ulcer medications. It reduces symptoms more quickly and heals ulcerations in the esophagus as well as stomach ulcers. The advantages of Losec for the individual are a healthier life with fewer side effects, fewer operations and shorter recuperation time. For the health care system, Losec provides significant savings due to shorter hospital stays and fewer physician consultations.

A large number of people contributed to the development of Losec. In addition to project manager Sven Erik Sjöstrand, chemist Ulf Ljunggren and chief researcher Ivan Östholm, the project involved around 150 researchers and technicians.

Losec is the most widely sold medication in the world. For four years in a row it had the largest sales figures of any medication on the world market. In 1999 sales were more than SEK 50 billion, and in 2000 they had reached SEK 66 billion, even though there were similar, less expensive preparations on the market. Through more than 200 million treatments given, Losec has improved the quality of life for patients around the world.

N E X I U M ®

Nexium® is AstraZeneca's successor to Losec®. It is a purified form of Losec based upon a simpler molecule. The USA was one of the largest markets for Losec. When the patent on Losec in the USA expired in 2001, the market was opened wide for less-expensive copies. AstraZeneca is trying to introduce patients to the new medication in order to reduce the market share available to competitors.

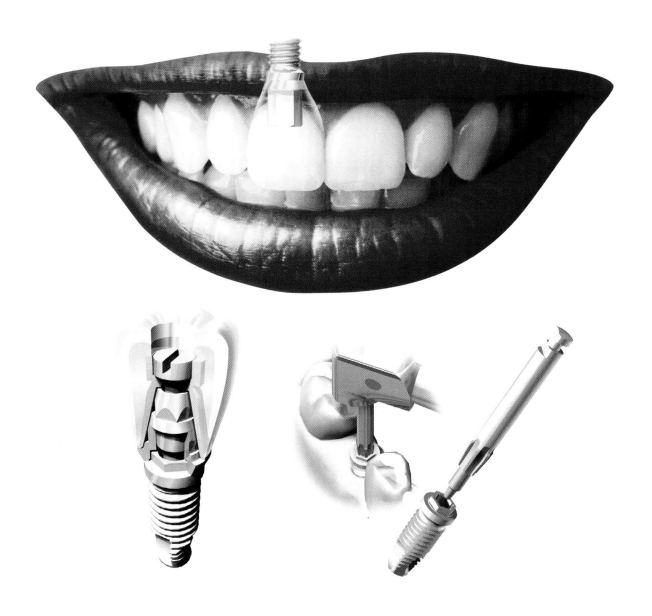

SINCE 1965 OVER HALF A MILLION DENTAL PATIENTS AROUND THE WORLD HAVE BEEN TREATED USING THE BRÅNEMARK® METHOD.
THE SURGEON IMPLANTS SMALL TITANIUM SOCKETS INTO THE JAWBONE, INTO WHICH THE ARTIFICIAL TEETH ARE
SCREWED. THE TEETH ARE SECURELY FASTENED AND FEEL LIKE THE PATIENT'S OWN.

BRÅNEMARK® SYSTEM

Per-Ingvar Brånemark, a professor of anatomy, developed a method for surgically inserting titanium screws directly into the bone. This method has proven especially useful in replacing lost teeth. Traditional dental solutions using prosthetics and bridges are not always satisfactory.

In the 1950s Per-Ingvar Brånemark had discovered that titanium can bond with human tissues and can thus function as an implant in the human body. Brånemark had been studying how blood is produced in the bone marrow and then moves out through the bone tissue and out into the bloodstream. In order to observe this process, he surgically implanted tiny microscopes made of titanium directly into the bodies of his subjects. When it was time to remove the microscopes they couldn't be removed. They had "taken root." Brånemark was struck by the possibilities of this discovery. His study showed that titanium had very special characteristics. While the body rejects almost all foreign materials, it will accept titanium. Titanium is a member of the family of light metals and is resistant to most acids.

In 1965 Brånemark performed his first tooth replacement on a patient. Since then over half a million dental patients around the world have been treated using the Brånemark® method. The surgeon implants small titanium sockets into the jawbone, into which the artificial teeth are screwed. The teeth are securely fastened and feel like the patient's own.

In addition to fasteners for artificial teeth and other prosthetics, this method has also been used in the development of facial prosthetics and hearing aids that are fastened directly to the bones of the skull. It promises new uses in other types of surgery as well.

ULTRASOUND

Helmuth Hertz (1920–1990) was born in Berlin. His studies were interrupted by the Second World War and after some years as a prisoner of war, Hertz came to Lund, thanks to the help of Danish physicist Niels Bohr and others. Hertz worked in the Department of Physics at Lund University, where he directed the construction of the university's first accelerator. In the early 1950s, Helmuth Hertz began the research into ultrasound for medical uses, which would later make him famous the world over.

At about this time, ultrasound had come into use as a means of testing materials. In this method, a series of ultrasound impulses are sent into a material, and the resulting echoes can then be interpreted, revealing for example holes and weaknesses in the material. The same principles are used in radar and sonar.

Physician Inge Edler told Hertz that he wanted a bloodless method for examining a patient's heart. Hertz hit upon the idea of using ultrasound. Over a period of a few days Hertz and Edler performed experiments with an ultrasound machine at the Technical X-Ray Center in Malmö. It took many years to fully develop the methodology, but echocardiography has revolutionized heart diagnostics.

In 1977 Hertz and Edler received the Lasker Prize, the American equivalent of the Nobel Prize in Medicine. The use of ultrasound in health care is constantly increasing in a number of areas.

Helmuth Hertz also developed a color ink jet printer that has been used chiefly for printing alphanumeric symbols, and especially for computer-generated images in color.

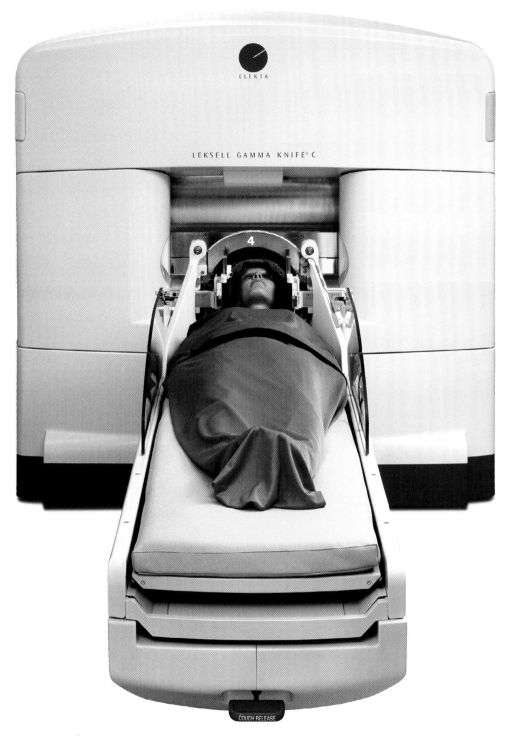

LEKSELL GAMMA KNIFE®, MODEL C WITH AN AUTOMATIC POSITIONING SYSTEM, APS. TOP RIGHT: THE FIRST LEKSELL GAMMA KNIFE.

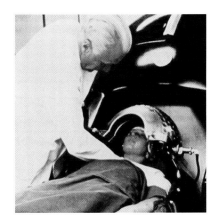

LEKSELL GAMMA KNIFE®

The Leksell Gamma Knife® is an ingenious tool invented by Lars Leksell (1907–1986) and Börje Larsson, who built the first prototype in 1968 for the private hospital Sophiahemmet in Stockholm. The prototype was sold to the USA in 1974 for the symbolic sum of SEK 1.

In contrast to traditional brain surgery, this is a noninvasive method. The portion of the brain where the disease is located is exposed to radiation. The "knife" delivers gamma rays through a helmet. With the help of a system of three-dimensional images and dosage metering, the helmet focuses the radiation on a specific target point in the brain, destroying the diseased tissue without damage to surrounding areas. The Gamma Knife is especially useful when the diseased area is located close to vital areas of the brain. In such cases, traditional surgery would put the life of the patient in danger.

A patient can often leave the hospital within 24 hours after a Gamma Knife operation. With traditional brain surgery, a patient may need to remain in hospital for several weeks. In addition, the cost of Gamma Knife treatment is lower.

Elekta, founded in 1972, is a world leader in the development and sales of linear accelerators used in radiation treatment for brain tumors and arterial malformations without opening the skull.

The market for this device is expanding rapidly, and its field of applications continues to grow. For example, it is used to treat comparatively common functional disturbances of the brain such as epilepsy and Parkinson's disease, eye cancer, cancer of the nose and chronic facial pain.

Elekta has calculated that in Europe, there are around 110 patients per million inhabitants afflicted by diseases that can be treated using the Gamma Knife. If functional disturbances are included, the numbers are considerably higher, both for the treatment of patients with a functional disturbance who have already been treated by traditional means, and for new patients.

In 1984 the first Leksell Gamma Knife for general clinical use was sold, and 1986 saw commercial sale of a Gamma Knife. Model B was introduced in 1988, and Model B-2 in 1992. A whole new generation was introduced in 1999: Model C with an Automatic Positioning System, APS. With the help of APS, the patient is automatically positioned and treatment time is reduced by 50–75% as compared to earlier systems.

The growth potential of this device is significant. At present the Gamma Knife is used in only 20% of the applications for which it has been clinically approved.

A "STROKES OF GENIUS" EXHIBITION HELD IN GOTHENBURG IN 2000. HERE, 12-YEAR OLD IDA LARSSON DEMONSTRATES HER ANTI-CRUELTY FLY SWATTER, WHICH IS SUPPOSED TO SCARE FLIES WITH A 'NEAR-DEATH' EXPERIENCE, RATHER THAN KILL THEM.

SOME ORGANIZATIONS

"Strokes of Genius"

The origin of the Swedish movement known as Snilleblixtarna ("Strokes of Genius") was the "Egg Drop" contest for young inventors started by inventor and entrepreneur Anders Rosén. He wanted to stimulate children's creativity and sense of initiative by letting them solve a problem on their own. Rosén hoped to awaken the children's interest for problem solving, technology and science through playful means not always found in school.

The first "Egg Drop" contests were staged at the Kristinedal Elementary School in Stenungsund on Sweden's west coast in 1991 and 1992. Children and adults competed to find the cleverest method for keeping an egg from breaking when it was dropped from a height of 25 meters. The result was that the children showed an incredibly rich inventiveness. Many of the children were more creative than the adult contestants.

Anders Rosén's experiences from this contest led to the formation of the Snilleblixtarna ("Strokes of Genius") movement in 1993. Rosén wanted to showcase the creativity of children by organizing inventors' exhibitions.

Children from 6 to 11 years old would be given the freedom to think up their own solutions to everyday problems they encounter.

Teacher Inga-Lill Ottoson of the Kristinedal School took up the cause and the first "Stroke of Genius Day" inventors' contest was held in 1994 with 22 children participating. An 8-year old named Angelica came up with the name "Strokes of Genius," which the children voted on in a name contest.

"Strokes of Genius" is based upon voluntary participation and a complete lack of limitations for the stimulation of the children's ideas and creativity. Their incredible creativity and thought processes are displayed to the adult world.

"Strokes of Genius" has now grown to a national movement with branches in many parts of Sweden and counterparts in other countries as well.

Mini-Entrepreneurs

The Mini-Entrepreneurs group was begun in 1997 by Anders Rosén. "Strokes of Genius" is a group for elementary school pupils, and works well with children from 6 to 10 years old. It's more difficult to interest children in the age group 11 and up.

Rosen's son had been a member of "Strokes of Genius" for several years. When he asked about a way of continuing, the idea for the Mini-Entrepreneurs (Mini-företagarna) was born.

The movement seeks to stimulate and develop children's creativity and ability to take initiative by encouraging them to start their own mini business. The group fills the gap between "Strokes of Genius" and the "Young Entrepreneurship" group for students of high school-age. Together these groups provide an unbroken chain of support for young inventors and entrepreneurs all the way through the education system, from elementary school up to college and university level.

Young Entrepreneurship

Young Entrepreneurship (Ung Företagsamhet) is an educational concept for high school students, which was imported from the USA in the 1980s. Its aim is to stimulate the creativity and entrepreneurial spirit of young people by increasing their understanding of the small business process. Young people are given a chance to refine their business skills by running a business.

"The Greenhouse"

Sweden also has a group for young innovators at university and college level called "The Greenhouse" (Drivhuset). This movement was started in 1992 by Fredrik Langborg and Christer Westlund, two students at the University College in Karlstad. The two felt the need for more room for students in the early stages of their college education to develop their ideas and design their own projects. The concept has spread to several universities and colleges in Sweden.

"Finn upp" inventors' competition for junior high school students

The idea for inventors' competitions for young people originated in Japan, where during the 1970s contestants from all over the world were invited to attend. In Sweden the then-named Board for Technical Development (STU) encouraged the Swedish Inventors' Association (SUF) and the Swedish Society of Engineers (ISF, a non-profit organization with a membership of about 150,000 engineers), to draw up guidelines for an inventors' contest in Sweden. The best inventions from this contest would go on to the Japanese competition. Sweden's first such contest was organized in 1979. All junior high school students in the nation were invited to participate. The competition was given the name Finn Upp, a humorous word play on the Swedish verb uppfinna ('invent').

The basis for this contest was a desire to show young students how important inventing is for the development of society. It was hoped that they might become more aware of the types of needs which exist, and that in trying to realize their own ideas, they would be able to experience the joy of creating something new. In doing all this, they would learn to make better use of technology and at the same time develop a greater interest in science and technology.

When the 1979 Finn Upp contest had ended, 632 inventions had been submitted. During Finn Upp 1983, a total of 1,926 inventions were received, nearly four times the number of the first year. Finn Upp 1985 received 4,593 suggested inventions, 38% of which were from girls. The percentage of girls participating in the contest continues to increase.

Finn Upp 2000 marked the eighth time the contest was staged. All Swedish elementary pupils in grades 6–9 were invited to take part. The next contest will begin in the autumn of 2002.

The Swedish Inventors' Association

The Swedish Inventors' Association (SUF) was formed on March 12, 1886, making it the oldest inventors' group in the world. The group's founder was Salomon A. Andrée, Chief Engineer at the Swedish Patent Authority. This was the same Andrée who ten years later made the famed trip to the North Pole by balloon. Other founding members of the Society included Otto Fanehjelm, Gustaf de Laval, Carl Setterberg and Ernst A. Wiman.

In its early years, SUF was mainly a social organization for the great Swedish inventors of the day, such as de Laval, Alrik Hult and Gustaf Dalén. Today the group plays a strong role in promoting Swedish industry by lending support to inventors. SUF has a number of local branches as well as corporate members.

Over the years, the world of inventing has clearly been dominated by men. In an effort to correct this imbalance and spotlight female inventors, QUIS (Qvinnliga uppfinnare i Sverige/Women Inventors of Sweden) was formed to provide a network for all women members of SUF. The group's goal is to emphasize the work of women inventors and to collaborate with other networks and organizations. In their 1986 study on 100 significant Swedish innovators, Torkel Wallmark and Douglas McQueen found only one woman, Birgit Dahle (see p. 47), who together with her husband Orvar Dahle invented the Pressductor transducer.

An analysis by S.A. Andrée in 1888 showed that during the period 1870–1874, women inventors accounted for only 1.3% of all patents granted in Sweden. A study by the Swedish Patent Authority in the year 2000 showed that women made up 5% of the patent-receiving inventors. Among members who have received SUF's highest honors, two were women: Ellida Lagerman (1863–1950) and Walborg Thorsell. Three of the recipients of SUF's honors plaque are women: Kerstin Gustafsson, Anna-Greta Werner and Ragnhild Löfgren.

A look at SUF's membership rosters shows an interesting development. Of 800 members in 1975, fourteen were women, or barely 2% of the membership. By 1999 this percentage had increased markedly: of 2,000 members, 550 were women or 27% of the total membership. In 2002 the number of women members is about

430 out of a total of 3,000, or about 14–15% of the total.

QUIS members have made significant contributions. Examples of inventions which have attracted particular attention include:

Simplified skin test for allergies

Nurse Kajsa Naenfeldt collaborated with Per Arne Sigurdsson to develop the "Kajsomat," a device for administering allergy skin tests. The Kajsomat makes it possible to perform all of the necessary "prick" tests at once rather than having to perform several.

A "short cut" to cells Doctoral researcher Sarah Fredriksson was working on the problem of introducing genes into a cell without disturbing or damaging it. She developed a method based on magnetic fields and magnetic particles which has been named "MagnetoPore." This method is gentle to the cell, allowing it to take on foreign molecules and genes while maintaining its integrity. MagnetoPore is used primarily in research and by the pharmaceuticals industry.

Cooling cap for cancer patients

Oncology nurse Yvonne Olofsson developed the Dignicap, which allows patients to undergo chemotherapy treatments without losing their hair. The cap is computer controlled to maintain the necessary temperature.

Anesthetic mask for infants

Anesthesiologist Monika Dahlstrand of the Blekinge Hospital in Karlskrona has developed an anesthetic mask equipped with a pacifier. The infant breathes in the anesthetic through its nose while sucking on the pacifier.

Mosquito and tick repellent

Chemist and researcher Walborg Thorsell has researched more effective repellents against mosquitoes. She has developed several different repellents, including Demidex and IxnIx.

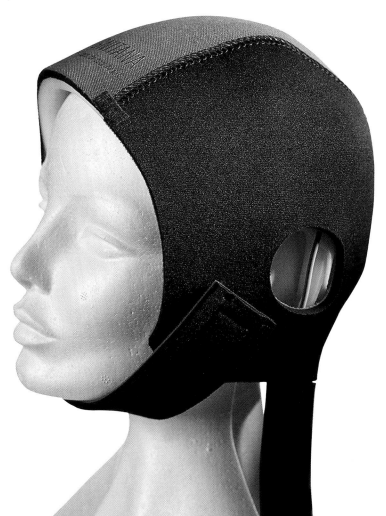

DIGNICAP COOLING CAP FOR CANCER PATIENTS, DEVELOPED BY ONCOLOGY NURSE YVONNE OLOFSSON.

DEVICES FOR PERSONAL ASSISTANCE

Many new inventions to assist people with functional impairments are being developed, e.g. the "Permobile" electric wheelchair (above) and the special adaptation of automobiles. However, such inventions are not often produced in mass quantities since many such solutions are tailor-made to suit the individual. One invention that has meant much for the disabled is the mobile telephone. It is interesting to note that with the introduction of the mobile telephone, many projects to develop aids for people with functional impairments were made obsolete.

Continued developments in mobile telephony and its combination with Internet services and perhaps even Global Positioning Systems (GPS) will provide important aids and improved quality of life to people with visual, auditory and mobility impair-ments and many others. The miniatur-ization of electronics and mechanical devices and their integration with human biology will also provide significant improvements. There are already prosthetic devices controlled by nerve impulses, e.g. artificial legs, hands and arms. It is likely that we will be able to treat many function-reducing diseases in more satisfactory ways than today. An example of work toward this end is Nobel Prize winner Arvid Carlsson's work to cure Parkinson's disease, schizophrenia, etc. by medically influencing the signal substances produced by the body.

Many inventions that we perhaps do not regard as aids for people with functional impairments make it possible for many to live a normal, active life which would not otherwise be possible, e.g. medications for treating heart conditions, blood pressure and asthma, pacemakers and dialysis machines.

Sweden is also a forerunner in preventing disability through preventative safety measures, for example seat belts, the rear-facing child safety seat and airbags. Other important Swedish inventions which help prevent congenital defects include ultrasound, fetal diagnostics and equipment for monitoring childbirth. Some of these devices make it possible to take measures to prevent future impairments at an early stage.

THE FUTURE

The future is of course impossible to predict. Many of the innovations that will be of importance in the next 10 to 20 years have already been invented. Developments are continually ongoing. Methodologies are refined, materials are made stronger, etc. Continual development means that ideas previously thought impossible may be realized.

It is difficult to know just which innovation will lead to a great leap in technology. Two historical examples of such inventions are the transistor and the laser. Although these "unexpected" innovations would have been difficult to predict, they changed the course of technological development.

Sweden will continue to be the birthplace of many significant innovations. One reason for this is that more Swedish universities are accepting research ideas for commercial purposes. Attempts are also being made to reduce the time needed to move from idea to finished product. Research and development takes place in "start-up" companies, research parks and university courses in entrepreneurship.

Sweden has a strong tradition in the field of biotechnology research. Thanks to the Swedish inventions of the ultracentrifuge and electrophoresis, gigantic leaps in knowledge are being made throughout the world. Examples include HUGO, the human genome project, as well as mapping of the genomes of animals and plants using molecular biology. These projects will lead to yet more innovations, as will multidisciplinary fields in which biology, IT, electronics and mechanics are integrated.

The Internet offers a means for the gathering of a hitherto unparalleled knowledge and power. Its capacity and uses will increase greatly, both for private use and for research and communication.

When the telephone became common in the early 1900s, many experts believed that the need for travel and letter writing would come to an end. In fact, the telephone had just the opposite effect. Today, 100 years later, as the Internet is becoming more widespread, banks for example believe that people will begin to stay at home and manage their banking from there. Will this really be the case or will the demand for banking services increase because of the Internet?

New developments and inventions will be made—not just in the fields of IT, biotechnology and electronics, even though these will indeed be important areas. Older "traditional" areas will benefit as well. 100 years have now passed since Jonas Wenström introduced his great inventions in electrotechnology, which became the basis for the electrification of industrialized nations. The beginning of this new century saw significant innovations in that same field by Mats Leijon that will lead to the continuation of the process of electrification and effectivization of the old electrical networks. (We should mention here that about 40% of the world's population still does not have electricity.)

Water shortages are a huge global problem, in particular shortages of drinking water, but also for other uses. In this area, Karl Dunkers has made use of new technologies for great contributions to the science of storage and purification of sewage water, as well as the storage of fresh water. However, there is still much to be done in this area before these problems are solved.

SOME OTHER SWEDISH INNOVATIONS

in chronological order

Coated Welding Rods: Oskar Kjellberg, around 1905.
Kanthal Incandescent Wire: Hans von Kantzow, 1926.
Insulin: Erik Jorpes, 1929.
Unitized Steel Auto Body: Gösta Nyström, 1929.
KaMeWa Propeller (Boat Propeller with Adjustable Blades), 1937.
AP or Dikumarol, Anti-blood Clot Medication: Jörgen Lehmann, 1939.
PAS Tuberculosis Medication: Jörgen Lehmann, 1943.
Free-wheeling/Front Wheel Drive for Passenger Cars: Gunnar Ljungström, 1945.
Portable Ticket Machine: Nils Ståhl, 1946.
Geodimeter: Erik Bergstrand, Ragnar Schöldström, 1947.
Submersible Pump: Sixten Englesson, 1947.
Circulating Pulp Digester for Paper Production: Johan Richter, Tyke Christenson, 1948.
Lightweight Concrete: Per Isaksson, 1948.
Climbing Building Crane, Self-operating: Elis Lindén, 1950.
"500" Voting System: Christian Jacobaeus and Axel Hultman, 1950.
Fully Automated Sugar Centrifuge: Oscar Magnusson, 1950.
Perstorp Flooring: 1950.
Position Sensing Detector: Torkel Wallmark, 1950.
Respirator: Carl Gunnar Engström, 1950.
WKE 4 High Alloy Cobalt Steel: Holger Jarleborg, 1950.
Fully Automated Production of Sugar Cubes: Åke Bireth Jensen, 1953.
Heart and Lung Machine: Clarence Crafoord, Åke Senning and P.A. Åstradsson, around 1956.
ASEA-SKF Method for Production of Steel: Walter Nordin, 1958.
Tape-driven Feeder: Isak Rosén, 1960.
Thermovision: Per Lindberg, Hans Malmberg, 1961.
Lamella Separator: Bengt Hedström and Åke Jernqvist, 1965.
Nicodur Grinding Wheel: Olle Lindström and Erik Lundblad, 1965.
RIST Allergy Test (Radio Immuno Sorbent Test): Leif Wide, Rolf Axén and Jerker Porath, 1966.
Dynamex, an Improved Explosive: Bertil Enoksson, 1967.
RAST Allergy Test (Radio Allergo Sorbent Test): Leif Wide, Hans Bennich and Gunnar Johansson, 1967.
ORIGA Cylinder: Bo Granbom and Gunnar Lundqvist, 1970.
Penglobe, Synthetic Penicillin: Bertil Ekström and Berndt Sjöberg, 1970.
Symmetrical Door: Eddy Lundin, 1971.
Dirivent and Optivent Fan Systems: Birger Lärkfeldt, 1972.
"Doppin" Robotic Linefeeder for Production Lines: Arne Rönnbeck, 1973.
Minirin, Medication against Diabetes Insipidus: Jan Mulder and Czech researchers, 1974.
Handheld Data Collection Terminal: Gerhard Westerner, 1975.
Bearing Frequency System for Signals over Electric Lines: Bosse Lindgren and Lykke Olesen, 1978.
Self-emptying Railroad Car: Hilding Månström, 1978.
Surface Heparanization: Olle Lamm, 1980.
Pergo Laminated Flooring: Sven Danielsson, Tommy Johnsson, Kent Lindgren and Nils-Joel Nilsson, 1988.
Lead-free Bullets for Firearms: Bo Jakobsson, early 1990s.
Ferroelectric Liquid Crystals for Flat Picture Screens: Torbjörn Lagerwall and Noel Clark, 1991.
Aqua Barrier: Sten Magnus Cullberg, 1997.
ID Card and PIN Code: Erik Rothfjell.

INDEX

INDEX OF NAMES

SOURCES

Andersson, P. Gunnar, Idé grundar industri. Carlssons. Stockholm, 1995.
Boken om uppfinningar. Forum. Borås, 1985.
Från idé till produkt, 2nd part. Ed. Birger Kock. STU and SUF. Stockholm, 1963.
Från idé till produkt, 3rd ed. Ed. Birger Kock. SUF. Stockholm, 1980.
Från idé till produkt, 3rd part. Ed. Birger Kock. STU and SUF. Stockholm, 1981.
Frängsmyr, Tore. Alfred Nobel. Swedish Institute. Stockholm, 2001.
Hult, Jan, and others, Svensk teknikhistoria. Gidlunds. Hedemora, 1989.
Isakson, Börje, and Johansson, George, Svenska snilleblixtar I o.II.
    Gummessons. Falköping, 1993.
Peterson, Alf, Swedish Pioneers of Technology—a Presentation of IVA's
    Commemorative Medalists. IVA. Stockholm, 1994.
Sedig, Kjell, Swedish Inventions and Discoveries. Fact Sheets on Sweden. Swedish
    Institute, 2000.
Svenskt biografiskt lexikon.
Wallmark, Torkel, and McQueen, Douglas, 100 viktiga svenska innovationer.
    Studentlitteratur. Lund, 1986.

SEK 1 = GBP 0.07, EUR 0.11 or USD 0.10 (average 2001)
Some metric and imperial measures:
1 billion = 1,000 million
1 km (1,000 meters) = 0.621 mile
10 millimeters = 1 centimeter = 0.3937 inch
1 metric ton (1,000 kg) = 2,204.6 pounds
1 kg (1,000 g) = 2.2 pounds

Photos: ABB (pp. 27, 42, 46, 74), Alfa Laval (p. 24), Jan Almerén (p. 89), Amersham Biosciences (p. 80), Torbjörn Bergkvist (p. 98), Jan Håkan Dahlström/Bildhuset (p. 50 and Back Cover), Dahlström Design (p. 54 right), Dignitana (p. 97), Chad Ehlers/Tiofoto (p. 30), Electa (pp. 92, 93), Electrolux (pp. 34, 36, 76, 77 and Inside Front Cover), Ericsson (p. 16, Telephone p. 58), First Light/EyeQnet (p. 28), Flymo Partner (p. 48), Gambro (p. 86), Jessica Gow/Pressens Bild (p. 20), Haldex (p. 73), Hörnell (pp. 62, 63 and Front Cover), Gunnel Johansson/Mira (p. 70), Sven Olof Jonn/Johnér (p. 40), Bengt-Göran Karlsson/Tiofoto (p. 11), Kirby/Getty Images (p. 32), Jess Koppel/Getty Images (p. 13), Philip Laurell/Johnér (pp. 12, 53), Lexel (p. 51), Linn Malmén/Pressens Bild (p. 88), Matton Bild (p. 78), Nasa/Pressens Bild (p. 38), Nobel Biocare (p. 90), Nobelstiftelsen (pp. 18, 21), Pressens Bild (p. 52), Kristian Pohl/Pressens Bild (pp. 60, 61), Magnus Rietz/Johnér (p. 23), Saab (p. 54 left and p. 68), Sofia Sabel/Pressens Bild (p. 94), Georg Sessler/Bildhuset (p. 83), SKF (p. 41), Gunnar Smoliansky/Bildhuset (p. 26), Snickers Workwear (p. 64 and Inside Back Cover), Stock Image/EyeQnet (p. 84), Swedish Match (p. 22), Tekniska Museet Stockholm (p. 8), Tetra Pak (pp. 44, 45), Carl Henrik Tillberg (p. 39 and Dynamite p. 18), Volvo (pp. 66, 72).

Web addresses: www.iva.se, www.kva.se, www.si.se, www.sweden.se, www.swedishtrade.se

Kjell Sedig (born 1950), Licentiate in Engineering, Innovation Technology, Chalmers University of Technology in Gothenburg, has contributed to various publications, including Boken om uppfinningar (The book about inventions). Forum. Stockholm, 1985.
The author alone is responsible for the opinions stated in this book.

© Kjell Sedig and the Swedish Institute
Editor: Inger Envall
Technical adviser: Bengt A. Mölleryd, IVA
Technical editing: Camilla Modéer, former Federation of Swedish Industries
Translator: Daniel M. Olson
Language consulting: Terry Williams

Graphic Designer and Picture Editor: Mats Hedman
Typefaces: A Caslon, Bell Gothic
Paper: Invercote Creato 260 g (Cover), MultiArt Silk 150 g
Printed in Sweden by Kristianstads Boktryckeri AB, Kristianstad 2002.
ISBN 91-520-0694-8